THE CREATION OF LIFE

THE CREATION OF LIFE

a cybernetic approach to evolution

A. E. WILDER SMITH
D. Sc., Ph.D., Dr. es. Sc., F.R.I.C.
Professor at the University of Illinois
at the Medical Center, Chicago

HAROLD SHAW PUBLISHERS
WHEATON, ILLINOIS

FIRST EDITION

ISBN 87788-144-8

LIBRARY OF CONGRESS CATALOG CARD NUMBER 78-133984

contents

All that is made seems planless to the darkened mind, because there are more plans than it looked for. . . . There seems no plan because it is all plan.

C. S. Lewis
in *Perelandra*

acknowledgments

It is a pleasure to make the following acknowledgments:

Dr. Julian Richardson, Assistant Professor of Electrical Engineering at the Middle East Technical University, Ankara, Turkey, was kind and patient enough to work through the total manuscript and make many constructive suggestions.

The Atlas Computer Laboratory Library, Harwell, England, afforded me hospitality during a fortnight's pleasant stay there in the summer of 1969. The members of the staff of the library unearthed many useful references for me in the course of our discussions.

The Library of the Middle East Technical University, Ankara, allowed me the use of its resources on several occasions, especially on the subject of consciousness and artificial intelligence. Also the library of Hacettepe University afforded me valuable assistance in tracing relevant works.

Last but not least, my good and patient wife worked carefully through the entire text, and helped in the compilation

of the index, besides managing a household of a temporary
character in Turkey, looking after four rapidly growing chil-
dren and being willing to put up with a fourth book in about
as many years.

Scripture references are from the Revised Standard Ver-
sion of the Bible.

foreword

We are experiencing an age in which science and its applications are supreme. Man had only to make up his mind to reach the moon, and within ten years of the decision he had touched down on the lunar surface several times and brought back samples for analysis. There would seem to be no limit to human achievement by the same technique if supplies of time and money were adequate.

In the wake of the application of the so-called scientific method, a monoculture of technical know-how has developed and is spreading rapidly around the globe. Knowing how to tackle a problem by the scientific approach is not, however, the only ingredient of the present scientific monoculture. A philosophy of life accompanies this technical ability. Science studies matter and is not very good at much else. And the study of matter has led many to believe that a wholly material universe is the only reality. For them, all problems and all solutions are purely material. This philosophy of life is known as *scientific materialism*. One of its branches of thought is Neo-Darwinism, and in the coming discussions we shall have much to say about scientific materialism and its offshoot, Neo-Darwinism.

In the wake of the application of the so-called scientific method, then, a monoculture flourishing on scientific materialism is spreading over the world. Only a few years ago, Turkey, where I have been privileged to teach, and where I have written this book, did not even have a postal system, let alone television, radio networks, modern hospitals or expressways. But Turkish religious belief was highly developed. With westernization, initiated under Kemal Atatürk, the dust of the ages is being blasted away by the hurricane of technology from the West.

An unavoidable part of this blasting process consists of the erosion of ancient customs and national culture as well as of religious beliefs and superstitions which have often been a hindrance to progress in the material betterment of a proud and ancient people. It was, and is, argued that the modern technical wizard from the West is usually irreligious, if he is not directly atheistic. It is what a man believes that makes or unmakes him. The westernizers concluded that, in Turkey at least, man's beliefs "unmade" him! The irreligious or atheistic technical wizard, who can improve standards of living overnight, cure diseases and lengthen life is, therefore, to be emulated not only in his technical wizardry but in his religious vacuum too. Since technical experts believe neither in God, angels nor devils, many have concluded that it must be unprogressive to hang onto belief in God or the supernatural if the modern atheistic scientist, the pioneer of such a huge success, does not.

The cold blast of technology has created a cultural and even spiritual vacuum in developing countries as well as in countries where science has reigned supreme for years. The only difference is that in developing countries the pace is so rapid and the change so radical that the generations are losing contact with each other. Of course, this is also happening in developed countries, but the acuteness of the problem is nowhere seen so clearly as in those countries which have been ripped out of the past ages by the scientific monoculture in one generation.

The end result of the invasion of scientific technology in both developed and less developed countries is the same. For example, in countries such as England and Scandinavia, it is quite common to speak of the present era as being a "post-Christian" one. In Muslim countries, where scientific materialism has been at work for a shorter period of time, the younger generation has already become estranged to much of the religious heritage of the past. To be sure, they stick to some of the outward forms of past religious culture, but without the conviction of their parents.

In the United States and Western European countries where scientific materialism has often laid hold of the younger generation, the following pattern is often observed: The teenage son or daughter, brought up in a sincere, religious family (whether it be Jewish, Christian or Muslim is of little importance for our purpose here, so long as the family had a genuine heritage of belief in a Creator and in a book on which their belief was based) is to be prepared for a position of leadership. For this he needs higher education, which may mean the study of science, languages or law. Let us say that our student chooses science as his field.

During his freshman year he rapidly discovers, as a result of the scientific materialism which is the basis of all scientific higher education today, that the whole supernatural structure of belief on which the stability and happiness of his family rested during his formative years, was just nonsense. If our student had been brought up in a Christian family he rapidly finds, for example, that the family Bible allegedly contains a mere collection of myths on creation, the flood, the prophets, and the life of Jesus Christ. Today's science teaches that human life did not arise with Adam and Eve. Rather, "pools of interbreeding genes" would allegedly better describe the scientific facts of our ancestry.

My son was informed only the other day in his optional religious instruction (given by a Protestant teacher who holds no belief in anything supernatural) that Jesus never claimed to be God for the simple reason he knew he was not. Nor did he perform any miracles. His disciples invented them to bolster their reasons for founding a new religion of which they would be the leaders. This emasculated religious instruction was based squarely upon current scientific materialism. Matter is everything. Spirit, therefore, does not exist. Anything which lies outside the scientific materialistic view of things is not to be taken seriously.

The result in the Western world has been a shift in cultural values and an increasing religious vacuum. Science is credible. Materialism is credible. Religion is not. The shocking fact is that most Christian and other religious leaders have been powerless to do anything to stem the floodtide of scientific materialism, except, perhaps, to cry, "Faith"!

In the sites of the ancient cultures of Asia, exactly the same process is taking place before our eyes, but at a much more accelerated pace. As the Western scientific monoculture explodes into their territories, young men and women are entering newly established universities, staffed by Westerners or Western-trained nationals, there to learn that the religious (and often cultural) heritages of the past are an obstacle in the path of the scientific steamroller. Most Western-trained teachers have no belief in any nonmaterialistic meaning of life at all. In fact, many of them believe, and teach, that the origin of life, and indeed, life itself, is one big accident which took place over millions of years.

If life is an accident, then why not treat it as such? The students in the developing countries and elsewhere have taken the cue more quickly than their teachers. If there is no divine plan or meaning behind life it becomes as cheap as an accident should be. Only last week in Ankara one student's right hand was blown off while he was in the act of throwing a Molotov cocktail on campus. Of two others who shot each other, one is now paralyzed with a bullet in the spine. The dean was clubbed, whether by students or by police, no one knows. Two other youths clubbed each other until one was dead. The killer apparently is a student in the faculty of *law*! If life is adequately explained on the basis of scientific materialism, then there is nothing supernatural about it in the least. Thus, after death, there will be no penalties for murder or violence. The materialistic *view* of life brings with it a superficial and, at the same time, brutalizing, lawless *way* of life.

Why have law and order deteriorated so rapidly in the United States? Simply because for many years it has been commonly taught that life is a random, accidental phenomenon with no meaning except the purely materialistic one. Laws are merely a matter of human expediency. Since humans are allegedly accidents, so are their laws. No wonder that the result of such teaching is a contempt for the courts and for all due order. The older supernatural views taught that life was a plan and a code, which needed for its government a plan of supernaturally given codes or laws.

The change of emphasis has been working in the institutions of higher education for over one hundred years. Now we are seeing its fruits on a worldwide scale in the unprecedented breakdown of law and order. The incredible fact is that today's political leaders have to set up commissions to inquire into the reasons for the running tide toward anarchy, when the real reason seems so simple, once we see it in historical perspective. We have taught that the very origin of life, together with its maintenance, is due to "anarchy" (randomness, lack of law and codes). Naturally, after the doctrine has been planted and has taken root, it will bear its fruit.

A religious vacuum has been created by the sweeping victories of scientific materialism, but what is to replace the real values which have been destroyed in the flood? It is here that the philosophies of Marxism-Communism find an excellent culture medium. For they offer an idealism of a materialistic kind which does, for a time at least, replace the ancient philosophies of less sophisticated forbears.

Let us be quite specific. It took Charles Darwin nearly a generation to develop his theory of biological evolution. By it he offered the intellectual world a purely naturalistic account of life's origin and development. As a corollary he was forced, much against his wife's will, to abandon his faith in the Christian revelation. Today it takes one semester of freshman biology to conduct a student through the same steps which, in a generation, unhorsed Darwin and his Christian faith. Throughout the world of higher learning these steps toward spiritual vacuum are being taken at an accelerated rate. The consequences are most acute where the formation of the spiritual vacuum has been most rapid. That is, the developing countries are the ones which suffer most at the hands of scientific materialism, even though they may be reaping richer physical benefits.

Perhaps the most disturbing factor about the modern worldwide revolution is the fact that scientific materialism is the basis of both Marxism-Communism as well as of most Western higher education. Scientific materialism is the common denominator. Science is successful. Science delivers the goods. Science recognizes nothing but the material. Science is right. Everything else is unimportant. That is the tacit argument today.

The Eastern world of Communism propagates this view blatantly as it uses its materialistic view of science to support state atheism. The Western world, particularly in the area of higher learning, takes the same stand, though less blatantly. The end result in both areas is identical! The universities of East and West are turning out a generation of graduates with a materialistic and anarchic view of life which flourishes in a spiritual vacuum.

And yet, for those with eyes to see, the very progress of materialistic science is showing how inadequate its own views are.

The very study of material sciences has brought scientists to the recognition of the fact that its own theories need revision. There is urgent need for the study of things transmaterial and transcendent. Perhaps as never before, science is being forced to recognize an urgent need for the postulate of a great intelligence behind the coding order manifest throughout our visible and invisible universe.

A great difficulty in dealing with this and allied subjects lies in the fact that the average layman is not presented with a coherent account of the content of new discoveries. These new discoveries are beginning to resurrect some of the most ancient beliefs of mankind with respect to First Causes. For years now, perhaps for almost one hundred, the ancient beliefs have lain buried for fear of the scientific materialist. Now, as we shall see in later chapters, the mummies are being brought to life. It is as if wheat stored at the time of the pharaohs is suddenly beginning to germinate in the light and warmth of scientific progress. But students still continue to come to colleges and universities where they lose faith in anything divine because the newest developments are often not interpreted and made relevant to them.

In view of the above appraisal of scientific materialism and its consequences the author decided some years ago to write a series of books with the goal of pointing out, in the modern scientific context, the various areas in which progress has been made by recent research toward recognition that scientific materialism today holds the key neither to the past nor to the future of scientific development. There is no longer any need for the Christian or the believer in God to hide, intellectually speaking, in the catacombs. Today true science supports the man who believes in a supramaterialistic view of life, the universe and its future.

The present work is the third in a series and examines the scientific materialistic attempt at explaining life's origin and meaning. It relates some of the discoveries in the area of origins to recent progress in cybernetics and the development of artificial intelligence. Thus the book is not intended primarily for the "average light reader" (whoever he may be) but for the student seriously contending with the problems presented by advanced study and their relationship to religious beliefs. In a nutshell, the book treats the premises of materialistic naturalism and weighs them against supranaturalism as bases for our *Weltanschauung*, that is, our view of life's meaning.

In the past it has been rather difficult for a student to arm himself quickly and reliably against the onslaughts of scientific materialism. The scientific materialists have, in recent years, exercised an almost absolute monopoly of the scientific press. The religious press has often shown itself unable to take up effectively the cudgels against this view of life. As a consequence it has been a relatively easy matter for materialistic scientific mentors to undermine the faith of young students armed with little factual information. The result has been a real "slaughter of the infants" as in Herod's day—a "slaughter" about as "heroic" as Herod's! For it is so easy, for those who know how, to make a student's immature religious belief look scientifically and philosophically naïve.

It is the purpose of this series of books to supply intellectual weapons for those who feel they need them and who wish to fight for their faith and intellectual honesty. The series sets out to show the transcendent nature of life's origin, while showing up the missing factors in Neo-Darwinism. It links this with the important modern concepts of the nature of mind and intelligence, showing the significance of the recent developments in artificial intelligence.

In conclusion, one indulgence is asked of the reader. The book draws its contents from many disciplines. No one author can be expected to be an authority in every field of learning. I do not claim to be that. Nevertheless I have attempted to synthesize widely separated disciplines into a unified whole in dealing with the origin and meaning of life.

introduction

MISSING FACTORS IN NEO-DARWINIAN
EVOLUTIONARY THEORY

Increasing numbers of scientists, particularly physical and mathematical scientists, are becoming doubtful as to the adequacy of the theoretical basis on which current materialistic Neo-Darwinian theory is based. Few today seriously doubt the so-called "fact of evolution." For it is a solid fact that random, nonliving chemicals have, somehow or other, become ordered during the passage of time. That is, they have developed highly complex living matter, a process which is rightly termed "evolution." It is not the factual development of matter itself which is now under review, but rather the theories which have been proposed to account for this development of order.

The whole subject is highly controversial. In fact, it is becoming increasingly difficult to treat it publicly at all if one treats it critically. Any questionings of "accepted evolu-

tionary theory" are often regarded, ipso facto, as obscurantist, or as efforts to "turn the clock back." In view of this
state of affairs it is necessary to define our terms carefully
before launching out onto the stormy waters surrounding the
theories behind biological evolution. In the following text the
"fact of evolution" will be treated as meaning solely that
random, nonliving matter has, in the passage of time, become
ordered until it has reached a state of complexity sufficient
to support the biochemistry of life as we know it today. The
question of any causative agents behind this development
does not enter into the consideration of this factual development of order.

In our present context it is not intended to use the term
"evolution" to mean primarily the conversion of a lower
species of an organism into a higher one in the course of ages.
Thus we are not primarily concerned here with the conversion of bacteria into frogs or with the development of men or
their ancestors from apes or their ancestors. We wish to use
the term "evolution" in its strictly etymological sense to
denote the development of increasing order in matter leading
up to abiogenesis (genesis of life from nonlife) ontogenesis
(development of the embryo) and phylogenesis (development
of species).

Somehow or other, order and life have arisen from nonliving matter and are still arising and increasing in the continuous reproduction we observe going on about us. Neo-Darwinians and others propose certain theories to explain these
observed facts of evolution from nonliving matter. It is these
general theories which are under review.

Entropy is defined as "a measure of unavailable energy."
Evolution (or reduction of entropy) within the above special
definition of the term, has occurred and is still occurring in
three easily recognized areas. First, at some time or times in
the past, life must have arisen from nonliving matter. Physical
life is not generally regarded as being eternal, for even the
earth, in common with the universe, must have had a beginning in time. This single or multiple process (according to

one's views on whether life arose once or many times in the past) is known as *abiogenesis, neobiogenesis* or *archebiopoesis*.

Since the time of Pasteur, few scientists believe that abiogenesis or the spontaneous generation of life from nonliving matter (without the mediation of previously living matter) takes place today. On the other hand, many scientists are endeavoring to produce life, or at least, to produce the intermediate products thought to have led up to life in the past, from nonliving material under laboratory conditions. These experiments represent attempts to produce life or its intermediate products nonspontaneously. For all experimental interferences with matter rob us of the right to designate an experiment as a "spontaneous" event. A truly spontaneous reaction must be independent of all intelligently manipulated changes of conditions. Neobiogenesis, spontaneous or not, falls into the first category of our classification of evolutionary processes.

Second, every higher organism passes through evolutionary processes during ontogeny, in the course of which it becomes progressively more complex from the zygote (fertilized egg) upward. This development represents the second or ontogenetical type of evolution. In the past decade, molecular biology has made enormous strides in elucidating the mechanisms behind the progressive ordering of matter in the living and reproducing cell, so that today we know more about the processes directing ontogeny than ever before.

Neo-Darwinian theory, coupled with modern biochemistry, has set out to explain both these types of evolutionary process. For example, abiogenesis is almost universally regarded as being a process based on normal, naturalistic, random chemical changes, leading to more complex molecules, gradually tending upward toward the "simple" living cell. Darwin himself put on record his willingness to accept some such theory of abiogenesis when he mentioned, in one of his letters, the possibility of such a process having taken place in some "warm isolated pond." And the processes behind ontogeny have been regarded as basically similar to those behind abiogenesis. Spontaneous, ordinary chemical reactions have been sorted out by natural selection to lead life further up the evolutionary ladder after abiogenesis. The random chemical schemes behind both processes are regarded as being, in principle, the same.

To these two types of evolution (within our definition of the term)—abiogenesis and ontogeny—may be added a third, phylogeny, also controversial. This third type of evolutionary process may be defined as that which is assumed to have occurred throughout the past ages and which has led to the variety and complexity of life as we know it today. It deals with the origin of species, and, like the other two types of evolution we have mentioned, is assumed to be based on the random factors of ordinary spontaneous chemical reactions. All three types of evolution may be regarded simply as various manifestations of entropy reduction.

The following text attempts to deal with the validity and adequacy of the Neo-Darwinian hypotheses in accounting for the three types of evolutionary process as defined above. Random (chemical) mutations followed by natural selection over huge time spans are proposed as the main causative agents behind biological nature as we see it today. The question is: Are these basic Neo-Darwinian tenets adequate to account for the complexity of biology as we see it? Do random mutations and chemical reactions followed by natural selection over huge time spans offer a total and all-embracing explanation of both the origin and development of life abiogenetically, ontogenetically and phylogenetically speaking?

RECENT WORK ON ABIOGENESIS (NEOBIOGENESIS, ARCHEBIOPOESIS)

Some Basic Considerations

It is, of course, a basic tenet of most experimental work being carried out in the field of abiogenesis today—the volume of current work in this area is increasing almost exponentially—that natural, random chemical reactions, with the addition of no exogenous or supranatural interference, led to the original, spontaneous (some say inevitable) appearance of life on the earth. The following citation is a typical example of this type of view:

> We must assume that it is possible to duplicate, at least to some extent, those processes [occurring on the primitive earth] in the laboratory. Implicit in this assumption is the *requirement that no supernatural agency "entered nature" at the time of the origin, was crucial to it and then withdrew from history.*[1]

Few scientists express their materialism so explicitly! This means that ordinary random chemical reactions, as we know them today in the laboratory, accounted *on their own* for abiogenesis and will do so again, partially or completely, in the laboratory today *if and when we can reproduce the correct reaction conditions.*

The scientific materialists are bending all their efforts to demonstrate that, if a reaction leading up to life can take place now, in laboratory reaction vessels, without supernatural aid, then proof positive has been effectively delivered that no supernatural agency was needed to produce life at the beginning, at archebiopoesis. Thus any synthetic, laboratory production of life in the laboratory, under what are presumed to be conditions resembling those on the earth when life arose for the first time, is heralded in many circles as driving the last nail in God's and the supernaturalist's coffins. Who needs God and the supernaturalist position if life on the earth can be effectively accounted for without either?

Before accepting this commonly assumed position let us consider the following: Is it not remarkable that this view is not generally recognized for what it is—an absolute contradiction? For all the efforts of the scientific naturalists to prove their point by the above mentioned method only serve, in fact, to verify the correctness of the supernaturalist position. For, is it not true that the scientific materialists are, in their experiment, applying intelligence and thought to the ordering of matter? Under the influence of intelligence they are hoping to produce living matter from its nonliving base. *This is precisely the supernaturalist point of view.* For the supernaturalists hold that intelligence brooded over nonliving matter, the dust of the earth, which then became organized up to life. The hypothesis that life arose may be expressed by the following equation:

$$\text{Intelligence (motor)} + \text{Matter} = \text{Life}$$

The pure mechanism by which intelligence works is not so vital as the fact that intelligence when "combined" with matter can lead to life today as well as in past ages. What is vital is that intelligence used the inherent chemical and physical properties of nonliving matter to lower its entropy sufficiently for life to ride upon it.

The only question to solve, once we have seen the importance of the above fact, is the origin of the intelligence. Where could such intelligence exist before the scientific materialist's intelligence started to mold matter? We look into this question of the existence of nonhuman, nonbiological intelligence and consciousness in later chapters of the present work.

It was often formerly held that, in past ages, the lucky, rare, chance reaction occurred and led up to life, and that it was by this "hit or miss" method that life quite unexpectedly arose on the earth. This position is different from the view adopted by many modern scientists, among them Kenyon and Steinman, who hold that the inherent properties of matter led inevitably, like a sort of predestination, up to life on the earth. The older view was justified on the basis that the long time spans during which such rare and unlikely reactions could have occurred made them, in fact, likely reactions.[2] The longer the time allowed for such chance reactions to occur, the more numerous they must have become.

In using this argument it is forgotten that the longer the time allowed for a *reversible* synthesis to occur, the more likely the *reverse* reaction, or decomposition, also becomes.

So that, in the last analysis, the use of the long time-span argument to render the rare, or chance reaction possible or even, as some say, inevitable, cancels itself out, for life's chemical reactions are usually reversible. Thus, long time spans would not only give more time for the lucky synthetic reaction up toward life to take place, they would also give more time for the "unlucky" decomposition reaction to occur, away from life, back to nonlife!

For this and other reasons many scientists today are tending to edge away from the older "rare and lucky reaction" hypothesis to account for abiogenesis, and are leaning to the view that the summation of perfectly common, normal, random chemical reactions, caused by the inherent properties of matter, led up to life in the past. It is assumed that this same process will inevitably lead up to life again today if we can duplicate the same primitive conditions that produced abiogenesis.

This view is the basis of the many recent efforts to simulate the origin of life in the laboratory, starting from relatively simple chemicals.[3] It is argued that even though it may not be possible to arrive at a self-reproducing organism in one reaction stage, yet, if the new approach is correct it should yield at least some identifiable intermediate chemical products, or stages, which would act as signposts along the chemical path leading up to life. Hence the enthusiastic reception given to Miller and others' work. These authors produced, by natural random reactions, products which may be thought of as being chemical intermediates on the way up to the production of living matter from nonliving chemicals.

Each success in this line of work is hailed as yet another milestone along the path to proving that life is a *natural* phenomenon which has arisen spontaneously from random reactions stemming from the inherent properties of matter. Accordingly, life owes no portion of its origin to the interference in nature of supernatural agencies. The creator of life is, in fact, nothing more than the inherent chemical and physical latent forces inherent in matter. It would be incorrect, according to these newer views, to maintain that any-thing such as "spirit" worked on matter to induce life. Rather, the correct way of describing the origin of abio-genesis would be that matter worked out its own properties, with the result that life arose.

However, to do justice to the genuine scientific work which has been accomplished in this area, it is necessary to focus our attention on some of the experiments carried out recently in the area of abiogenesis.

Experimental Work on Abiogenesis

The whole subject of abiogenesis is at present in the throes of rapid development. Only a few years ago it would have been correct to state that no American college or university offered any adequate course on the subject of abiogenesis. Today graduate seminar courses have been given at Pennsyl-vania State University and also at San Francisco State Col-lege. Stanford University offers a regular catalog course on the subject.[4] The chemical origin of life is treated, at least briefly, in most introductory biology, zoology and micro-biology courses. If the trend continues, increasing numbers of colleges and universities inside and outside the United States will be offering courses on abiogenesis within the next decade or so.

The number of research papers on the subject has been increasing almost exponentially since the International Union of Biochemistry devoted its first volume to this subject in 1957.[5] It is thus high time that the technical and philosophi-cal aspects of this subject be treated from a point of view which demonstrates that abiogenesis is not the domain of the scientific materialists alone. It is in the field of abiogenesis that the inadequacy of the purely materialistic standpoint stands out so clearly.

Since 1957 the Biophysical Society, the American Asso-ciation for the Advancement of Science, the American Chemical Society and the Chemical Institute of Canada have all devoted special sections of their annual meetings to seminars on abiogenesis and chemical evolution. But as far as the author is aware, the defects and missing factors in the purely materialistic interpretation of this subject have not been specifically treated.

Reference is made to these developments to emphasize how actively the subject of chemical evolution and the origin of life is being investigated. But seldom does one see a clear, unmistakable reference to the fact that there might be an alternative and even a superior interpretation to the materialistic one.

Oparin and others justify this almost feverish activity in the area by the perfectly reasonable statement that it will not be possible to understand life fully without understanding its origin.[6] Such statements, although true, assume their true significance only in context. It must be remembered that Oparin, a leading Communist scientist, would be interested in any scientific proof that life is a purely materialistic phenomenon; that no supernatural agency such as God or a Creator was at work when life started and—as a corollary—that no supernatural consequences (such as judgment after death), will be involved after human life ends, either in the individual or as a race. Thus the whole question of the correctness of materialism or theism is involved in this problem of abiogenesis and scientific materialism.

What has been said about the relationship of common random chemical reactions to the origin of life may also be said of the maintenance and further evolution of life. The almost universal view today is that ordinary chemical reactions are entirely responsible for the maintenance and upward evolution of life. It is alleged that no supernatural agency is necessary to account for the facts of either process. Recent work in molecular biology has involved intensive investigation of these chemical processes, and has found them to be explicable on the same chemico-physical basis as that used to interpret the reactions of nonliving matter. Therefore, argue the majority of investigators today, if both the origin and maintenance of life are purely physical, chemical, material phenomena, why postulate anything more? If the Neo-Darwinian hypothesis adequately explains all the phenomena (abiogenesis and maintenance of life) we have examined, then let us be consequential in our thinking—as well as intellectually honest—and do as the Communists did long ago: Eradicate *all* the superstitious religious paraphernalia from our philosophy and become thoroughgoing materialists. We have been admonished to revise our thinking in accordance with this scheme of things for many years now. The result is that many believers in God are under intellectual duress. Some capitulate, while others put religion and intellectual honesty into two separate watertight compartments and somehow maintain this schizoid scheme in their daily lives. In view of the fact that many are showing signs of yielding to the apparent weight of evidence against mankind's oldest religious beliefs, it is imperative that someone present the facts which testify against the purely scientific materialist position.

There is no doubt about the fact that the scientific materialist position has been propagated in scientific and other circles in recent years to the almost total exclusion of the older supernaturalist position. This third book in the present series attempts to point out that there is, in fact, a very real missing factor in the Darwinian and materialistic hypothesis and to demonstrate what this missing factor is. Since the writing of the first book in the present series the whole subject has rapidly advanced. The present work is therefore intended to be complementary to *Man's Origin, Man's Destiny*.[7]

To many scientists there appears to be overwhelming evidence that the Darwinian and materialist views of life are adequate. In spite of this, many of the younger generation are becoming more and more convinced that these views do lack certain crucial factors. With Eden, Weisskopf, Schützenberger and others, they believe that the discovery of new natural laws or phenomena is needed to supply the crucial factors.[8]

The present volume attempts to take a further step in resolving this riddle by showing that the postulated new laws and factors sought are in fact, already known, but have not as yet been synthesized into our schemes of scientific thinking.

But before new hypotheses can be set up, old ones have to be thoroughly demolished. No one will listen to new hypotheses until he is convinced that the old ones are inadequate. It must also be remembered that scientists are as fallible as the rest of the human race. If an older scientist has become respected and famous as a result of his deveopment of certain theories, he will not easily relinquish those theories and with them his claim to fame in the field. It is hard and humiliating for even the best of us to admit that we were wrong.

This is, then, a continuation of the work of demolition attempted in the first volume of the series. Part I of the present text is concerned with the thankless task of criticism and demolition. Part II concerns itself with the examination of new theories to replace those demonstrated to be inadequate in the first half.

The nature of the proposed synthesis is as follows: Computer scientists are actively working on the problem of artificial intelligence and have already thrown a good deal of light on some of the basic functions of the biological nervous system. Computer science has widely succeeded in electronically simulating the biological nervous system. Although the mechanism by which a suitable computer achieves its artificial intelligence is different from that by which the brain achieves its intelligence, yet the end results are in some cases very similar, as we shall see later.

It is important to realize that processes which simulate human thought are no longer bound to biological nervous tissue and oxyhemoglobin. They can ride on entirely inorganic electrical systems. For the first time in history, intelligence has been experimentally separated from biology. Artificial intelligence, created by man, is riding on entirely inorganic systems of an apparently impersonal nature. Consequently, for the first time in history it is no longer necessary to believe in an anthropomorphic "old man in the sky" as the supernatural intelligence behind the universe.

In the last chapters of this book an attempt is made to synthesize some of the newer findings of cybernetics and artificial intelligence with evolutionary theory and its problems. These developments would seem to supply at least some of the laws and phenomena believed to be missing in Neo-Darwinian theory.

It is the author's view that *thought and information processes* comprise some of the missing factors in Neo-Darwinian thought. It is, for example, the biochemists' thought processes and information supply which will probably lead up to the synthesis of life from nonliving matter in the laboratory. In other words, the synthesis of life will depend on the inherent properties of matter as well as on the information supply derived from the scientist who directs these inherent properties.

If this "information (or thought) directing chemical reactions" idea is the true basis of synthetic, experimental life in the laboratory today, why should it not have been the basis of abiogenesis in the past—assuming the principle of uniformitarianism is valid? This concept has several advantages over the Neo-Darwinian schemes current today. First, it describes accurately the method by which all experimental scientists are trying to create life from the nonliving in the laboratory. Scientists apply their thought and information supply to flow sheets and realize them in attempting to direct the inherent properties of nonliving matter up to the living state.

Second, this scheme of things corresponds significantly to the account of creation in the Scriptures. The Creator is reported to have taken "the dust of the earth" and spoken over it. That is, he expressed his thought processes through it in his formation of a living man. This procedure represents the action of motor intelligence or thought processes on the chemical and other inherent properties of nonliving matter.

The assumption of thought processes which are not of human origin behind abiogenesis would thus complete our understanding of the basic causes behind the appearance of life. The suggestion is that the synthetic efforts at the laboratory production of life are really an attempt to think the Creator's thoughts after him.

Again, the proposals we are making here have the advantage of being experimentally verifiable, which is more than can be said of many Neo-Darwinian proposals on origins. If we can show that motor thought plus the chemical reactions of matter lead up to life in the laboratory, we shall then have experimental proof that our proposals on original abiogenesis by the same process, but on a much larger scale, are not all rubbish. In this way it is hoped to achieve at least the beginnings of a synthesis comprising the problems of archebiopoesis and those of cybernetics and artificial intelligence.

The subject is ambitious as well as highly controversial. No one is more deeply aware of his lack of qualifications to deal with certain aspects of artificial intelligence than the present author. He therefore begs the indulgence of the real mathematicians and cybernetic experts. It is, however, his hope that, in risking an attempt at this synthesis, others better qualified than he may be stimulated to take up the problem and solve it more fundamentally.

1. Dean H. Kenyon and Gary Steinman, *Biochemical Predestination,* p. 30.

2. Cf. A. E. Wilder Smith, *Man's Origin, Man's Destiny,* pp. 63-70.

3. S. L. Miller, *Science* 117 (1953): 528; and *J. Amer. Chem. Soc.* 77 (1955): 2351; and A. I. Oparin, ed., *The Origin of Life on the Earth*, p. 123.

4. Kenyon and Steinman, p. X.

5. Oparin, *The Origin of Life on the Earth.*

6. Oparin, *Life: Its Nature, Origin and Development*, pp. 1-5.

7. Wilder Smith, *Man's Origin, Man's Destiny.*

8. See articles in Paul S. Moorhead and Martin M. Kaplan, eds., *Mathematical Challenges to the Neo-Darwinian Interpretation of Evolution.*

PART 1

1.
missing
factors
in
neo-darwinian
thought

"There is a pretty widespread sense of dissatisfaction about what has come to be thought of as the accepted evolutionary theory in the English-speaking world, the so-called Neo-Darwinian theory."[1] So said Sir Peter Medawar in his opening remarks as chairman of a symposium entitled "Mathematical Challenges to the Neo-Darwinian Interpretation of Evolution" held April 25 and 26, 1966, at the Wistar Institute of Anatomy and Biology, Philadelphia.

In the course of his remarks, Sir Peter mentioned that this dissatisfaction came from three main quarters and was an expression not only of scientific dissatisfaction but of malaise in other quarters as well:

> First of all, religious; where once the complaint was that evolution happened at all, now the complaint generally is that it happens without Divine motivation. Many of you will have read with incredulous horror the kind of pious bunk written by Teilhard de Chardin on this subject. . . .

Sir Peter then went on to mention that over and above the religious objections to the theory, there are the philosophical and methodological ones which have been aired by Professor Karl Popper, who believes that *any* real or even unreal evolutionary episode that we care to think up is capable of being explained by the Neo-Darwinian hypothesis. This is supposed to demonstrate that the theory is too wide and too general to be of practical use as a guideline in scientific thought and research.

MISSING FACTORS

Concluding his remarks, Sir Peter rightly said that the only objections to evolutionary theory about which the scientists care are the truly scientific ones. These real scientific objections were the actual basis for the convening of the symposium. The burden of them all was that there are missing factors in present-day evolutionary theory. Obviously, if vital factors are missing in any theory, its usefulness must be reduced. The theory becomes too general and flabby to afford concrete guidelines for constructive, progressive thought and experiment. Some of the scientists present expressed their conviction that the missing factors in Neo-Darwinian thought were indeed vital factors.

However, it became rather obvious during the course of some of the proceedings that certain other scientists, notably older-generation biologists, were determined to treat with impatience, scorn and even ridicule, certain younger men who voiced views conflicting with those of the present biological establishment. This was particularly the case when certain new knowledge gained from cybernetic research was cited as throwing into focus the gaps in Neo-Darwinian theory. Indeed, almost throughout the proceedings, an undercurrent of irritation and impatience was felt toward scientists who think it necessary to reexamine such allegedly well-established foundations as those upon which modern biological theory is built.

NATURAL SELECTION INADEQUATE

M. Schützenberger, in the course of the symposium, maintained that a basic cause of the concern mentioned lies partly in the Darwinian concept of randomness. He held that there is "a serious gap in the current theory of evolution."[2] Schützenberger believed that if this gap could be filled, Neo-Darwinian theory would be less dependent on the postulates of random mutation and natural selection in its efforts to account for the facts of biology. He said that it is fundamentally and mathematically unsound to attempt to explain the incredibly orderly systems of the biological world solely in terms of random mutations and natural selection. These two latter principles may play some minor role, but they should not be overloaded, as they are at present, in being assigned the main role in evolutionary theory. They need the support of new principles if evolutionary doctrine is to be placed on a mathematically sound basis.

In addition Schützenberger pointed out that recent developments in computer science have shown that the spontaneous evolution of a self-replicating organism is a phenomenon which has never been duplicated or simulated successfully even on the largest and most rapid computers available to date.

THE SITUATION IN NUCLEAR PHYSICS

V. F. Weisskopf, Professor of Physics at the Massachusetts Institute of Technology, speaking on the same subject, remarked:

> I feel that the situation in evolution is rather to be compared with the situation in nuclear physics where we would like to look at it from all sides, *because there is some suspicion that an essential point is still missing.* . . . If I wanted to be nasty toward the evolutionists, I would say that they are surer of themselves than we nuclear physicists are—and that's quite a lot.[3]

RANDOMNESS INADEQUATE

M. Eden, Professor of Electrical Engineering, M.I.T., as well as Schützenberger, found a source of concern in the Darwinian concept of randomness as a source of the order revealed in biology. Eden wrote on this problem:

> It is our contention that if "random" is given a serious and crucial interpretation from a probabilistic point of view, the randomness postulate is highly implausible and *that an adequate scientific theory of evolution must await the discovery and elucidation of new natural laws—physical, physiochemical and biological.* Until such time, Neo-Darwinian evolution is a re-statement of Darwin's seminal insight that the origin of species may have a naturalistic explanation.[4]

These recent doubts about the theoretical basis of evolutionary theory are concerned largely with the role played by random processes in the Darwinian scheme of things. Such processes are, of course, basic to the original idea of explaining the observed extraction of order from random systems on a naturalistic foundation. However, not only have fundamental random processes been called into question. Other vital Darwinian principles have been examined critically in recent years.

SIGNIFICANCE OF VAST TIME SPANS

It has been customary to attempt to overcome some of the basic problems of extracting order from randomness by assuming the availability of huge time spans during which random processes could maneuver themselves toward direction and order. A citation from John Kendrew demonstrates how this idea of huge time spans is employed to get around the implausibility objection:

> It may be surprising that a random process like this can improve a species, or even produce a new species, indeed lead eventually to the whole vast diversity of animal and plant life we see around us. But it must be remembered that these processes have operated over an enormous span of

time, more than five hundred million years.[5]

Statements such as Dr. Kendrew's are typical of the Darwinian and Neo-Darwinian position on the key role of large time spans in the spontaneous extraction of order from random systems.

However, this second foundation stone of Darwinian thought has been called into question too, notably by H. Blum who, though he can scarcely be suspected of being an anti-Darwinian, takes a strikingly contrasting view to that of Kendrew and the majority of Darwinians on the significance of long time spans and their role in evolutionary processes. Blum has pointed out that *the time factor can be entirely irrelevant to evolution in biological systems of the type envisaged by Kendrew and other evolutionary scientists.* He states:

> "I think if I were rewriting this chapter [on archebiopoesis, or neobiogenesis] completely, I should want to change the emphasis somewhat. *I should want to play down still more the importance of the great amount of time available for highly improbable events to occur. One may take the view that the greater the time elapsed the greater should be the approach to equilibrium, the most probable state, and it seems that this ought to take precedence in our thinking over the idea that time provides the possibility for the occurrence of the highly improbable.*[6]

Blum's conclusion is well drawn. The Neo-Darwinians have often totally overlooked this concept of equilibrium. Increasing the time factor in reversible reactions merely increases the chances that equilibrium rather than the improbable will be reached. Living biochemicals are highly improbable structures. Thus, increasing the time span allotted to a reversible reaction will bring increasing equilibrium—not the increasing complexity which leads to life. Blum is very careful to point out that the energy reaching the surface of the prebiotic earth would not, so far as we can tell today, have altered this state of affairs.

NECESSITY OF ENERGY SOURCES

Sidney Fox's symposium volume, *The Origins of Prebiological Systems*, endeavors to solve the problem of prebiological sources of energy which could have shifted chemical equilibria upward, to account for molecular and biological complexity. Blum's argument concerning systems reaching equilibrium with the passage of time would be modified if it were proven that available energy could be fed into such a system, reducing entropy at the cost of this available energy. Obviously, a human zygote does not normally reach equilibrium with time. It grows in complexity. It is allowed to grow because coupled available energy is fed into it, overcoming its normal tendency to decomposition which would occur if the zygote's metabolic motors, its enzyme systems, were not working.

The fact remains, however, that there is, at present, little evidence that in the prebiotic world such systems as those proposed by Fox and others could have supplied the available coupled energy necessary to reverse the process of reaching equilibrium. There is a large and growing body of evidence that quite complex organic molecules can arise in random systems which are supplied with various forms of energy. There is, however, less evidence that molecules of the complexity of viable proteins and enzymes could be so formed. This problem will be treated more fully later.

NATURAL SELECTION

Finally, a third principle of Darwinian thought has come under fire in recent years. It is the principle which is considered to have given direction to evolution and is regarded as one of the great seminal insights which Darwin gave the scientific world. It is the principle of natural selection. Speaking of this principle, Eden maintains,

> Concepts such as natural selection by the survival of the
> fittest are tautologous: that is, they simply restate the fact

that only the properties of organisms which survive to produce offspring, or to produce more offspring than their
cohorts, will appear in the succeeding generations.[7]

Apart from the concept of the survival of the fittest
being considered tautologous, an even more serious charge
against the importance of the principle behind natural sexual
selection is being raised today. J. Brun's work, reporting that
the hermaphrodite nematode *Caenorhabditis elegans* can
adapt to elevated temperatures if it is given eight to ten generations to accustom itself to each ½° step, is cited as an
example by Eden.[8] Since this nematode is self-fertilizing, sexual selection presumably cannot be invoked to explain this
progressive adaptation. This fact can be construed as casting
doubt on the necessity of natural sexual selection in the
achievement of adaptation, direction and speciation in evolution.

It is of no use for critics to argue that sex merely *accelerates* genetic selection and that adaptation under asexual conditions will simply be slower than that taking place under
conditions of sexual selection. Darwin himself attributed a
major role, not a minor one, to sexual natural selection.
Thus, the attempt now made to regard natural sexual selection as a much faster process gives the impression of hedging
or withdrawing in the face of new and contradictory evidence.

The upshot of all these facts and criticisms is that some
basic tenets of Neo-Darwinian theory are under fire, and
heavily so. We attempt to weigh this and other evidence more
fully in later chapters.

Leaving the question of basic tenets and theories behind
Darwinism, we now turn our attention to some practical experimental matters which have an important impact on
theory. We must consider the origin of the basic chemical
building blocks of life and ascertain how far these can be
accounted for by random processes. After that we turn our
attention to the possible origin of the more complex chemical substrates of life.

1. P. S. Moorhead and M. M. Kaplan, eds., *Mathematical Challenges to the Neo-Darwinian Interpretation of Evolution,* p. XI.

2. Ibid., p. 73.

3. Ibid., p. 100.

4. Ibid., p. 109.

5. John Kendrew, *The Thread of Life*, cited in ibid., p. 8.

6. H. Blum, *Time's Arrow and Evolution*, p. 178a.

7. Murray Eden, article in *Mathematical Challenges . . .* , p. 7.

8. J. Brun, "Genetic Adaptation of *Caenorhabditis elegans (Nematoda)* to High Temperatures," *Science* 150 (1965): 1467, as cited in *Mathematical Challenges . . .* , p. 6.

2.

abiogenesis:
its postulated
mechanisms

RANDOM SYSTEMS POSTULATED AS LEADING TO
ABIOGENESIS—THE ORIGIN OF BIOMONOMERS

In dealing with theories concerned with the origin of life
from nonliving materials we must first settle the question of
the origin of the chemical building blocks, or biomonomers,
of which living materials are constructed.

All living material is constructed of relatively simple chemical biomonomers, which, like building blocks, couple or
string themselves together with other biomonomers in specific patterns to yield the macromolecules which bear life as we
know it. These biomonomers comprise such simple organic
molecules as amino acids, heterocyclic bases, porphyrins and
other substances. How did these biomonomers arise from
nonliving materials and string themselves together, or poly-
merize, to yield the structures on which life rides?

This issue is one in which confusion often reigns, even
though the answers as to the possible origins of some of the

basic biomonomers of life are well known today. About one hundred scientific publications have appeared in the last few years to deal with this question. The burden of most of them is that many biomonomers can arise spontaneously from their constituent elements under random conditions thought to be similar to those which obtained on the primitive, pre-biotic earth. This point should be kept clearly in view in all discussions on the origin of biomonomers. For, although the basic building blocks of life, the biomonomers, can and do appear under spontaneous, random conditions, it is very much less clear how huge and specific macromolecules arose for life to ride on.

This is not to say that large macromolecules can never be formed under random conditions. For it is well known in circles specializing in protobiology that even-sequenced pep-tides (chains of amino acids), which may have biological significance, have been produced under chemical conditions similar to those thought to have existed on the primordial earth. No nucleic acids were present when these sequenced peptides were formed.[1] And it must be remembered that sequenced peptides are still a long way off from sequenced viable proteins.

It is in making this distinction between the formation of the biomonomers of living structures and the formation of such molecules as hemoglobin, chlorophyll and nucleic acids by random processes that the parting of the Neo-Darwinian and supramaterialist ways occurs. The usual tactic of the Neo-Darwinians is to accuse any scientist of ignorance when he ·suggests that although biomonomers may occur sponta-neously, the supermolecules of viable matter do not. In one recent publication on this subject I saw that a highly irate scientific materialist had written in the margin: "The author is obviously ignorant of the recent fifty to one hundred pub-lications on abiologic synthesis in the laboratory." In reality the author had simply stated that although biomonomers do arise spontaneously, the specific sequenced proteins on which life rides do not.

SPONTANEOUS SYNTHESIS OF BIOMONOMERS

In experiments on abiological synthesis of the type first carried out by Miller and then repeated in many different forms and under varying conditions by later workers, it has been adequately demonstrated that various biomonomers may be formed spontaneously.[2] These biomonomers have been interpreted as being intermediate steps in chemical evolution leading up to life.

An excellent review of this type of experiment has been given by Dean H. Kenyon and Gary Steinman.[3] In the same work there is a good account of the so-called Haldane-Oparin hypothesis of the origin of life from simple random chemical reactions by entirely natural processes.

It is important to realize that the Miller type of experiment on abiogenesis does not aim at the production of full-blown bacteria or other "simple" forms of life by passing an electric discharge through a mixture of ammonia, methane, steam and perhaps some inorganic salts. It aims rather at the production of simple chemicals or biomonomers by random means, the formation of which could be interpreted as demonstrating a trend toward life from nonlife in chemical evolution. Thus, the spontaneous formation of amino acids in a nonliving random medium is interpreted as a first step up from nonliving matter to living matter by entirely naturalistic mechanisms with no supernatural intervention. It is pointed out that this conclusion is justified simply because amino acids are building blocks of life and amino acids arise spontaneously.

Today no one expects total spontaneous generation of life to occur in such experiments. But, since Miller's work, many scientists expect the initial evolutionary chemical steps to be taken which, if continued in the same direction, would lead to the spontaneous generation of life from nonliving material. Spontaneous amino-acid formation is uniformly interpreted in this way. It is allegedly the first step in a long, spontaneous chain of chemical reactions leading up to living matter. (See Fig. I.)

Scheme Showing the Role of Spontaneity and Direction
in the Development of Life from Chemical Elements.

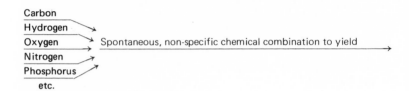

Carbon
Hydrogen
Oxygen   Spontaneous, non-specific chemical combination to yield
Nitrogen
Phosphorus
    etc.

Biomonomers (or basic building blocks of life). Increasing directional

specificity to yield sequenced, coded biodimers, biotrimers and

biopolymers culminating in the macromolecules of life: Enzymes,

DNA, RNA, Ribosomes. As specificity increases so the role

played by spontaneity decreases. Co-ordinated, specific metabolism

developing between specific macromolecules, leading up to the

specificity of protocells. Further specific development to the living

cell. Further specific development leading to multicellular

organism, based on further complex coding sequences. Multicellular

organisms. Further coding, resulting in higher plants, animals,

primates and man.   Conscious Man.

All upward development is based upon more complex coding, that is, on less
randomness and more coding order and sequences. The origin of coded messages
lies in intelligence and intelligence is based upon work expenditure. Thus the
whole upward evolution of life must be based upon intellectual work expenditure
to meet the requirements of thermodynamics and information (and coding)
theory. Darwinian theory does not provide for this work requirement, but com-
mits it to the vagaries of randomness and non-specificity. Thus the missing factor
in Darwinian Theory is connected with directional energy requirements which are
not accounted for as theory stands at present.

Figure I

The techniques developed by Miller and his colleagues have led to the isolation of many chemical building blocks of life which are present in living material and which are formed spontaneously from simpler substance. We must now look into some of the specific results obtained by this experimental approach to abiogenesis.

SPONTANEOUS SYNTHESIS OF BIOMONOMERS—AMINO ACIDS

By sparking together methane, ammonia, hydrogen and water, the synthesis of such biomonomers as glycine, alanine, β-alanine, sarcosine and α-amino-butyric acid has been reported.[4] Aspartic acid and asparagine arise from simple reagents using cyanoacetylene as intermediate.[5] By using a simple gaseous mixture of ethane, ammonia and water and treating it with Hg-sensitized ultraviolet radiation, glycine, alanine and α-aminobutyric acid, formic acid and propionic acid have been formed.[6]

Aspartic acid, threonine, serine, glutamic acid, proline, glycine, alanine, valine, alloisoleucine, leucine, tyrosine, phenylalanine, α-aminobutyric acid, β-alanine, sarcosine and N-methylalanine were formed as a result of heating methane ammonia and water at 950° C. in the presence of quartz sand.[7]

More complex heterocyclic bases, such as adenine, have been produced by the irradiation of ammonia, methane and water by electron beams. Even certain porphyrins have been produced by extensions of the above method.[8] The type of energy source used in these experiments does not appear to be critical in deciding the end products produced. The heterocyclic base and porphyrin syntheses carried out according to a similar experimental scheme are described more fully in a later section.

All the above biomonomers can be produced quite easily by spontaneous chemical processes under conditions thought to approximate those believed to have prevailed on the primitive, prebiotic earth. It has been concluded, therefore, that extension of the same line of approach will show that even the macromolecules of life can be arrived at by the same basic random process.

SPONTANEOUS SYNTHESIS OF BUILDING BLOCKS—SUGARS

Amino acids acting alone as building blocks or biomonomers would be insufficient for the generation of life. Sugars of various types are also necessary, since they enter into the processes of living macromolecules. It is thus our next step to look into the possibilities of spontaneous formation of sugars in random chemical processes.

It has long been known that sugars may be easily synthesized from formaldehyde.[9] In fact, the simple solution of formaldehyde in an aqueous base will produce spontaneously a mixture of sugars.[10] Fructose, cellobiose, xylulose, glycolaldehyde, galactose, mannose, arabinose, ribose, ribulose, xylose, together with glyceraldehyde, hydroxyacetone and some tetroses have been isolated by this method.[11]

The initial reaction leading to all these sugars and hydroxy compounds is probably that involved in the synthesis of formaldehyde itself, which is apparently a slow reaction. When two formaldehyde molecules react together they form glycolaldehyde which, in turn, reacts with another formaldehyde molecule to form glyceraldehyde. These later condensations appear to be autocatalytic. Some 50 percent of the reacting formaldehyde may be converted in the above manner to glycolaldehyde.[12]

In the presence of calcium oxide or ammonia, similar reactions can be carried out at 50° C. or lower. At room temperature in the presence of suitable concentrations of ammonia there is a gradual and continuous buildup of sugar products in the reaction mixture.

SPONTANEOUS SYNTHESIS OF BUILDING BLOCKS—HETEROCYCLIC BASES

We have now accounted for the spontaneous synthesis of two important types of building blocks of life—the amino acids and the sugars. Another fundamental building block necessary for the synthesis of certain macromolecules of life is the class of compound known as the heterocyclic bases. We have already mentioned these biomonomers briefly under the heading dealing with amino acids.

Adenine is an essential heterocyclic base and is present in adenosine triphosphate (ATP) and nucleic acids. It has been found to arise spontaneously in aqueous solutions of ammonium cyanide when they are treated with heat for one day or longer. Adenine also arises when ammonium cyanide solutions are kept under suitable conditions at room temperature.

Along with adenine, these other interesting compounds arose: 4-aminoimidazole-5-carboxamide (AICA), 4-aminoimidazole-5-carboxamidine (AICAI), formamide and formamidine.[13] Ammonium cyanide (9.9 M) heated at 90° C. for one day yielded 60 mg./litre adenine. At the same time glycinamide, glycine, alanine, aspartic acid and some polymerized hydrocyanic acid were obtained. Ultraviolet light also favors the production of adenine from ammonium cyanide.[14] Adenine has also been obtained by electron bombardment of a gaseous mixture of methane, ammonia, hydrogen and water.[15] Details of the reaction mechanism proposed to explain these syntheses are found in Kenyon and Steinman.[16]

Thus there is little difficulty in assuming the spontaneous synthesis of heterocyclic bases necessary to serve as building blocks for the synthesis of life from nonliving material.

SPONTANEOUS SYNTHESIS OF BIOMONOMERS–PORPHYRINS

Porphyrins are present in such fundamental living structures as cytochromes, chlorophyll and hemoglobin. Their availability by spontaneous synthesis on the prebiotic earth is, therefore, of great importance and interest in dealing with the mechanism of abiogenesis.

When pyrrole and benzaldehyde are heated together at 180° C., they combine to form $\alpha, \beta, \gamma, \delta$-tetraphenylporphine and $\alpha, \beta, \gamma, \delta$-tetraphenylchlorin.[17] Aldehydes are easily formed under conditions thought to be similar to those obtaining on the prebiotic earth. Pyrroles arise easily by passing

electrical discharges through mixtures of acetylene and ammonia.[18] Thus, if sufficient acetylene and ammonia were
present in the prebiotic atmosphere, electrical discharges
passing through it would provide the porphyrins required as
building blocks for living structures. Similarly, irradiation of
pyrrole and benzaldehyde dissolved in pyridine, using an
X-ray source (cobalt [60]), produced porphyrins after the addition of zinc acetate as a catalyst.[19]

Although the role of porphyrins in hemoglobin, chlorophyll and cytochrome synthesis is well known, it is not yet
clear to the protobiologists whether these substances were
vital for the appearance of life on the earth. They certainly
are essential for oxidation-reduction reactions in living materials today and provide for the supply of energy for the living
cell. But some think that this may not have been the case in
very primitive life where other substances may have substi-
tuted for the porphyrins. It is assumed that the porphyrins
became important only in later, more developed, life forms,
but were not vital in primitive abiogenesis.

THE SYNTHESIS OF LIFE FROM ITS BUILDING BLOCKS

It is commonly taught today that the chemical building
blocks of the type mentioned above were probably formed in
the atmosphere and then washed down by rain from this or
other sites into the prebiotic seas where they accumulated.
Here, as the concentration of these biomonomers gradually
increased, various types of reactions occurred by which they
became strung together into chains or polymers. We must
glance at these reaction types for they too are assumed to
have taken place spontaneously, just as the building blocks
themselves are believed to have arisen.

The chemical reactions which are thought to have been
responsible for the stringing of the biomonomers together are
those known as polymerizations and condensations. The
nitrile group is a particularly fertile radical for reactions of
this type, for it possesses a triple valency bond across which
numerous chemical reactions readily take place. As long ago

as 1875 E. Pflueger suggested that life began with a cyanogen molecule since this substance so easily undergoes transformations of this type to yield, in Pflueger's words, "labile proteins."[20] Since Darwin's time, scientific materialists have argued that, because biomonomers are so easy to produce spontaneously, and since further reaction leads to more complex forms (such as occur with facility if a nitrile group or cyanogen molecule is present) the whole gamut of reactions leading up to specifically sequenced viable proteins may occur by the same mechanism.

In Darwin's age it was not known that the biomonomers could be formed so easily, although a good deal was known about the general composition of proteins. The sequences which are the source of protein specifically (together with variations in amino acid content) were less well understood. Scientists of that day firmly believed that once the biomonomers of life were available, the rest of the problem of the construction of the macromolecules of life would be simple. It would consist of one spontaneous reaction taking place after another. Supernatural guidance or interference was not seen to be necessary.

However, scientific knowledge today is radically different. Today scientists have worked out at least some of the thermodynamics of the construction of viable proteins and nucleic acids from their building blocks. The thermodynamics of these synthetic reactions leading up to specifically sequenced proteins not only demand energy but also involve nonrandom, specific, directional processes.

H. Blum in his work entitled *Time's Arrow and Evolution* demonstrates how entirely unsatisfactory the "random" approach is when it comes to solving the problem of the specificity of the macromolecules on which life rides.[21] The random approach is perfectly satisfactory when dealing with the origin of biomonomers themselves, for their structure and specificity are dependent on the inherent order of their constituent parts. But there is little evidence that amino acids and other simple biomonomers possess an inherent order (see later under Kenyon's work) which would be sufficient to guide them right up to macromolecules, such as hemoglobin, with no exogenous aid. Blum's cogent arguments have been treated in a previous work.[22] We examine this important problem again later.

For our present purposes it suffices to remember that although Blum is certainly not an anti-Darwinian, he comes to the firm conclusion that it is highly implausible to expect *building blocks* to arrange themselves spontaneously into the ordered and serried ranks of viable molecules exhibiting specific sequences such as we find in living matter. There are no theoretical difficulties about the spontaneous formation of the building blocks themselves, for this order is merely the outworking of a hidden order inherent in the constituent atoms and radicals. Blum and perhaps the majority of scientists concerned with this area of endeavor do not believe that simple biomonomers possess such a hidden order which would or could guide them right up to the stereospecificity of living macromolecules. For the living material of proteins and DNA is so highly ordered and complex that its spontaneous marshaling out of randomness is simply implausible.

In addition to this problem, Blum goes on to cast doubt on the once almost exclusively popular theory which propounded that huge time spans would allow even the most specific marshaling of viable chemical structures to take place spontaneously—a matter to which we have already alluded.

We have now arrived at the position at which we can maintain that biomonomers can and do arise spontaneously from their basic elements by virtue of their built-in chemical and physical properties. We have also arrived at the position where we find some qualified scientists doubting whether the biomonomers, once formed, are capable of polymerizing autonomously to form the specific macromolecules on which life rides. This subject is so involved that we shall be obliged to devote a whole section to it later. All we can risk saying at present is that the large macromolecules of life are not likely in theory, nor have they been observed in practice, to arise spontaneously without any exogenous aid. The exogenous aid we are thinking of here is that of enzymes or of intelligent manipulation of reaction conditions.

It is important that no misunderstandings arise at this stage in our reasoning. It must be emphasized that spontaneous combinations of biomonomers such as amino acids do occur and may lead to proteinlike substances. In fact, experiments to this effect have been reported.[23] By this means, substances called proteinoids have been actually isolated. However, proteinoids are a long way off from real biological proteins. For example, they show no antigenicity with the guinea pig, rabbit or uterine strip tests. In many cases these proteinoids were not even 100 percent hydrolyzable in either acid or base—a grave defect. In addition, their molecular weight varied from 3600-8600 which is, of course, for a protein, very small. In other words, the properties of the proteinoids derived from the random, spontaneous condensation of biomonomers are different from the properties of the proteins we meet in nature.

SPONTANEOUS BIOMONOMERS BUT NO
SPONTANEOUS SEQUENCED PROTEINS

The reason for this state of affairs—biomonomers may arise spontaneously while specific polymers are not likely to—is not hard to find. Very few stages in the reaction chain leading to alanine from its constituents are required. It is as if atoms "just could not miss" the alanine structure! The properties resident on its constituent atoms are such that "everything just falls into place." Put another way, if one constructed a jigsaw puzzle of just three pieces it could very easily be fitted together. The chances of putting it together wrong are minimal. However, in a puzzle of many thousands of pieces, many of which are practically identical, the problems of putting it together correctly multiply as the number of similar pieces increases. The simple biomonomers are to be compared with the three-piece jigsaw puzzle, while the viable macromolecules are represented by the puzzle containing thousands of almost identical pieces, each of which must be put into a highly specific position to complete the picture correctly.

There is, however, another aspect to the problem of building macromolecules and biomonomers.

ENTROPY "HOLES" AND ENTROPY "MOUNTAINS"

Theoretically and experimentally we know quite well that, under certain conditions, building blocks of the amino acids, adenine, sugar and other simple types can be formed spontaneously. These biomonomers represent, as it were, "entropy holes" into which elements easily "fall" if one "knocks" (activates) them hard enough with a "blow" of sufficient energy.

When we proceed further up the scale of order in chemical molecules and reach entities of larger size, such as viable proteins, then somewhat different conditions apply for their synthesis. These larger molecules are the "molecular houses" of which living cells are constructed; they themselves are made of the simpler building blocks or biomonomers. Such specific viable proteins are not put together as easily as the biomonomers. "Knocking" biomonomers around with supplies of random energy does not cause them to combine together in the specific manner that life demands. The proteins of life are represented by "entropy holes," just as the biomonomers are "entropy holes." But there is a difference. For the "entropy holes" which represent viable proteins are situated high up on the "entropy mountains." Being so "high up" in entropy status, it is difficult to coax chains of amino acids into these "holes" in the sequence we desire and which life demands.

It is relatively easy to coax a mixture of the elements carbon, hydrogen, oxygen and nitrogen into the building-block association we call an amino acid. The latter is an "entropy hole" lying in the "entropy lowlands"—like a low-lying lake on a golf course for which all golf balls ever driven on the course seem to possess a natural homing instinct! It is easy to hit a ball in almost any direction—it will eventually land in such a lake! The low-lying lake represents an entropy "hole" such as a biomonomer.

The situation is, however, somewhat different when considering the "houses," the macromolecular proteins, which are built up of the simpler amino acids. The proteins are to be compared with lakes lying very high up on the mountainsides surrounding the golf course. In fact, these lakes lie so high up and are so hidden in the mountains that it is difficult to aim a golf ball so that it will land in them. In the first place the sheer energy required to drive them up to such a hidden lake is considerable. Second, the direction given to the drive must be exceedingly accurate to hit the exact target. The two factors must be kept steadily in view when considering the formation of the specific macromolecules of life; the sheer *force* required to lower the entropy status sufficiently, followed by accurate *direction*.

We have arrived, then, at the position where we can account for the production of biomonomers by spontaneous mechanisms. Any release of energy in random mixtures of the required elements is liable to hit such low spots. But to hit the high-lying hidden "lakes on the mountainsides" is a different matter. The chance of hitting them is remote.

It will be necessary for us to return to this subject when we consider the theories put forward by S. W. Fox on abiogenesis. Meanwhile we must turn our attention to the actual chemical mechanisms by which biomonomers string themselves together to form larger molecules of both a random and a specific kind.

1. G. Steinman, *Arch. Biochem. Biophys.* 119 (1967): 76; and 121 (1967): 533; and Steinman and M. N. Cole, *Proc. Natl. Acad. Sci.* 58 (1967): 735.

2. S. L. Miller, *Science* 117 (1953): 528; and *J. Amer. Chem. Soc.* 77 (1955): 2351.

3. Dean H. Kenyon and Gary Steinman, *Biochemical Predestination*, pp. 1-301.

4. Miller, *J. Amer. Chem. Soc.* 77 (1955): 2351.

5. R. A. Sanchez, J. P. Ferris and L. E. Orgel, *Science* 154 (1966): 784.

6. W. E. Groth and H. V. Weyssenhoff, *Planet. Space. Sci.* 2 (1960): 79.

7. K. Harada and S. W. Fox, article in S. W. Fox, ed., *The Origins of Prebiological Systems*, pp. 187-93.

8. A. Szutka, article in *The Origins . . .* , pp. 243-51.

9. A. Butlerow, *Comp. Rend.* 53 (1861): 145; and *Ann.* 120 (1861): 295.

10. O. Loew, *J. Prakt. Chem.* 33 (1886): 321; and *Chem. Ber.* 22 (1889): 470.

11. E. Marian and O. Torraca, *Intern. Sugar. J.* 55 (1953): 309.

12. W. Langenbeck, *Angew. Chem.,* 66 (1954): 151.

13. J. Oro, *Biochem. Biophys. Res. Comm.* 2 (1960): 407.

14. C. Ponnamperuma, article in *The Origins . . .* , pp. 221-35.

15. C. Palm and M. Calvin, *J. Amer. Chem. Soc.* 84 (1965): 2115.

16. Kenyon and Steinman, p. 150.

17. R. H. Ball, G. D. Dorough and M. Calvin, *J. Amer. Chem. Soc.* 68 (1946): 2278; and P. Rothemund, *J. Amer. Chem. Soc.* 58 (1936): 625.

18. A. I. Oparin, *The Origin of Life*, pp. 127-30; and J. B. S. Haldane, *Rationalist Annual*, 3 (1929).

19. Szutka, pp. 243-51.

20. Cf. Kenyon and Steinman, p. 160.

21. H. Blum, *Time's Arrow and Evolution*, p. 178a.

22. A. E. Wilder Smith, *Man's Origin, Man's Destiny*.

23. S. W. Fox, K. Harada, K. R. Woods and C. R. Windsor, *Arch. Biochem. Biophys.* 102 (1963): 439; and *J. Amer. Chem. Soc.* 82 (1960): 3745.

3.

mechanisms
for macromolecular
synthesis

(Chapters 3 and 4 may be skipped by readers who dislike the intricacies of chemistry.)

Before we can proceed further we must look at the mechanisms by which the building blocks of life combine with one another. The chemistry of life is often of a very specialized kind. But even though it may often be specialized, it is subject to the perfectly normal laws of chemistry as found in chemical research in the laboratory.

DEHYDRATION, CONDENSATION AND POLYMERIZATION
OF BUILDING BLOCKS

Amino acids and other building blocks present in the macromolecules of living matter aggregate to form larger units mostly by reactions called condensations. The combinations usually involve the elimination of one molecule of water between two combining molecules. It is the removal of this molecule of water which presents the major difficulty in some condensations of biological significance. For, the removal of this water molecule from between two combining molecules requires energy which must therefore be supplied in some fashion.

A further difficulty arises in this question of the elimination of water. For, in the prebiotic world, it is assumed that the condensation reaction took place in the presence of a large excess of water which would tend, according to the law of mass action, to hinder the condensation process and to facilitate the decomposition or splitting process. This means simply that the large excess of water present would be likely to hinder condensation reactions which tend to go upward to the formation of macromolecules. The more water, the less condensation.

Assuming, however, that the condensation reaction does take place, the energy requirements are expressed as follows:

$$\Delta F^{\circ}_{298} = 3 \text{ to } 4 \text{ kcal at the dipeptide level.}$$

If the reaction is to proceed in the direction of the dipeptide, the water molecule formed must be removed from the reaction system since the reaction is reversible. If it is not removed the concentration of water building up in the system will hydrolyze the dipeptide back again to the constituent amino acids, as hinted at above. The energy absorbed in the formation of the dipeptide would be released again if this reverse hydrolysis took place. The result would be *no synthesis*.

Chemically speaking, there is nothing mystical about the mechanism by which such reactions can lead to the most complex proteins. So long as water is removed from the system, and energy supplied, the synthesis will go forward spontaneously. This is why some scientists regard life simply as a mechanism involving condensation with the removal of water and the supply of energy.

But the experimental facts of this condensation show us that the mere mechanism outlined above is insufficient to account for the *specificity* of life's processes. Mere condensations with the supply of energy do not account for everything. An ordinary chemical condensation will, if it takes place, certainly lead to more complex molecules and polypeptides. But these structures will not necessarily consist of the purely sequenced, specific types which alone are viable. Besides dehydration and the supply of energy, another factor—that of *direction*—must be taken into account, as mentioned earlier.

We conclude then, that not only must purely chemical and energetic factors be considered in the origin of the macromolecules of life. The question of the direction given to purely chemical matters must be accounted for too. Many modern scientific materialists believe that even this question can be solved by appealing to natural, random causes. Some believe that the direction is inherent in the biomonomers themselves with the result that they can direct themselves because of some kind of inner order they possess. Others believe that the direction came from catalytic reactions taking place on the surface of natural minerals such as clay. It will be necessary to treat this aspect of the source of the specificity and direction in natural synthesis in a special section.

Exactly the same considerations of energy and direction apply to the other chemical mechanisms which life uses to build up its macromolecules. Pyrocondensation, polymerization and other reactions involving amino acids, polymetaphosphates, etc., not only need to have their energy requirements met. They all possess mechanisms for achieving this. In the production of large molecules in which many reaction pathways are possible, direction as well as order is needed to attain the specificity of viable chemicals.

MECHANISMS FOR OBTAINING DIRECTION IN SYNTHESIS

In principle there are two basic mechanisms by which

direction can be introduced into a multistaged synthetic reaction. The first involves the use of a *specific catalyst* which, by its intrinsic properties, induces a reaction not only to move faster but also possibly to take a specific direction. Although they are used very widely indeed in many industries, such catalysts are often not fully understood as far as their mechanism of action is concerned. They often introduce much larger surface areas on which reactions may take place. Many natural substances, such as clays, quartz sands, etc., do, under some conditions, not only act as reaction accelerators, they also introduce specificity (direction) into multistage synthesis. Some scientists believe, therefore, that the building blocks of life assembled themselves on the surfaces of catalysts such as natural clays to produce the specific macromolecules needed by living cells.

The second basic mechanism by which order and sequence specificity can be introduced into a multistage macromolecular synthesis is by *intelligent manipulation of the reaction conditions* by the scientist presiding over the reaction. We shall need to look into both methods of achieving direction in synthesis.

VARIOUS VIEWS ON THE ORIGIN OF DIRECTION AND SPECIFICITY IN SYNTHESIS

That direction in synthesis leading to proteins is an unavoidable necessity is revealed by the experimental results obtained where no direction is applied. Only by taking such results into account can one obtain a balanced view of the vital nature of direction in synthesis.

As an introduction to this rather complex subject let us first use an illustration. Waves and wind can account for the ripples and indentations formed on the sand of the seashore. Waves and wind are energetic phenomena of a more or less random character. Together they make marks in the sand, sometimes with and sometimes without pattern. We might risk the statement that there is often some sort of recognizable pattern which arises as a result of wind and waves.

However, it has never been known in all the history of man, or even in prehistory (fossil evidence), that wind and waves produced any writing, or any of our signatures engraved in the sand. They can produce many patterns but not the pattern we call writing. If we were taking an early morning walk by the seashore and found our signature boldly written in the sand, it would never occur to us to attribute it to anything else but intelligence. Some types of pattern, such as those produced by the ripples of the waves, do not necessarily demand explanation in terms of intelligence. On the other hand, some types of code pattern of a higher type such as a writing, are, in our experience, only explicable in terms of a controlling intelligence.

Biomonomers are like the ripples on the seashore sand, for there is an analagous simple type of order in both. *However, DNA and RNA molecules, together with those of some viable proteins, display the code characteristics of writing*. Both represent a definite, orderly code which conveys *information* to a code reader. There is in writing, and also in genetic codes, a higher, altogether different kind of order than that in the ripples on the seashore sand—or in biomonomers. If I come across ripples on the seashore during my early morning walk, I exclaim, "Ah, the delightful clean wind and the surf. How beautiful are the ripples in the sand!" And that is just about the only message I see in the patterns in the sand. But if I see my name boldly written in the sand, or if I see, "John loves Mary," an entirely different reaction takes place within me. I gain information which is conveyed to my own intelligence by the written message. Only a human intelligence could be behind such a pattern.

The order found in life consists, for our present purposes, of two main types. The first is that kind of order found in the sand ripples by the seashore; this is the kind of order found in the biomonomers which are at the base of all material order supporting life. The second kind is that found in the coded information written on the sequenced strands and spirals of the DNA and RNA molecules. For this latter order contains the syntactical sequenced order of a type resembling the code in a written sentence.

DNA and RNA molecules are long threads consisting of spiral chains of sequenced biomonomers. The sequences hide a code which gives information and instructions for the synthesis of the proteins on which life rides. The information is contained in the form of a four-letter language of the type *abcacddcabaacdbbcad*, etc. which goes on for thousands of letters. The exact sequence order of a protein's amino acids is "written down" in the sequence order of this four-letter language on the threads of the DNA strands in a pattern similar to the arrangement of the letters of our alphabet in a sentence. It is the *order* of the sequences of our alphabet letters which conveys the information in code form. Thus, the letters *n, d* and *a* convey information which varies according to the sequence in which they occur. When they occur in the order a-n-d, their meaning is different from when they occur in the sequence d-a-n. Some sequences may be nonsensical, for example a-d-n or n-a-d. To a modern biochemist the sequence d-n-a is as full of meaning as the sequence n-d-a is empty.

It is clear, therefore, that the letters remain the same. But the sequence of the letters decides the information conveyed in this type of order. The synthesis of each protein in the body is controlled by its gene, which is a stretch of DNA thread containing the genetic order sequences which act as a template for the synthesis of particular protein molecule sequences. That is, the sequences of amino acid biomonomers occurring on a protein are decided by the sequences of the four-letter alphabet on the gene thread. Three DNA "letters" are needed in sequence for each amino acid biomonomer on a protein sequence. This means that it takes three hundred DNA "letters" to provide the instructions for the synthesis of a protein sequence of one hundred letters.

From this it is clear that the method by which we write our names in the sand by using sequences of a twenty-four-letter alphabet to convey information as to our identity is quite similar in principle to the method used by the cell to convey information to the ribosomes (where the synthetic work in the cell is executed) to ensure that specific protein syntheses are carried out. The analogy between writing our names on the sand and writing information on the genes is close. Both involve information coding by means of sequences.

Thus it would be just as much of a shock for most of us to be asked to believe that the random movement of molecules and atoms caused by random energy has spelled out the genetic code on the DNA molecular thread sequence as it would if we were asked to believe that our names were spelled out on the sand by the random action of the sea and the wind. Both the written code on the seashore and the genetic code of the genes are, at least to the unprejudiced, unmistakably *codes*. Surely the order of any code betrays to any perceptive individual the unmistakable signs of intelligence or thought! As surely as the unexpected name written on the sand at the beach leads any unprejudiced person to postulate an intelligence, so the writing on the threads of the genes forces us to assume *thought* behind them. For coded information *is* a form of thought. It manifests thought. Codes of any type are inconceivable on any random basis because *thought is not random in its nature*.

In order to establish this point still further, let us do a small calculation. Imagine the odds involved in assuming a random explanation of a code. Consider a simple 400-letter gene and let us assume that a monkey is set to pound away at a genetic typewriter in an effort to spell out our coded 400-letter gene, using only blind chance to do so. He has the simple four-letter genetic alphabet at his disposal. The odds against his getting the correct order for the first sequence are four to one. The odds against getting the second sequence right are sixteen to one. The odds against getting the first three sequences right are sixty-four to one. One can work out his chances for getting the rest of the 397 sequences correct. For a simple gene of only 300 sequences the "odds against" have been calculated as one followed by 130 zeros, to one.

It is, then, small wonder that most scientists have come to the conclusion that sequenced DNA and proteins cannot be attributed to chance alone. Direction must be arranged for somehow. If "blind chance" is excluded then we must be dealing with "weighted" or "directed" chance which is a contradiction in itself.

MECHANISMS BY WHICH DIRECTION, SPECIFICITY AND CODING MAY BE INTRODUCED

One of the methods by which blind chance in the stringing together of biomonomers may be reduced is by causing the condensation reactions to take place on the surface of a catalyst.

Sydney W. Fox, whose research on abiogenesis we have already mentioned, is among those scientists who suggest that the coding and specificity of natural molecules could have originated on the surface of natural catalysts. Fox and others realized that amino acids would, in the first place, scarcely undergo condensation reactions, except in very small amounts, in ordinary cold, dilute, aqueous solutions. The solutions would have to be very hot, or water would have to be excluded altogether and heat applied to the dry mixtures of biomonomers. Second, a natural surface of a catalytic nature would have to be present to reduce random condensations which would be devoid of specificity, or would show too little of that commodity, and increase chemical direction and sequencing.

With this in mind Fox experimented with hot lava taken from volcanic areas and found that it caused easy condensation of amino acids to give proteinoids. Further, he found that the amino acid sequences of these proteinoids were not totally random. For the chemical composition of the proteinoids formed varied from that of the original mixture of amino acids. In other words, a slight amount of selectivity had been exercized which reduced the reactivity of some amino acids and increased that of others.

It is clear that the sequential order on these proteinoids is nothing compared with that resident on natural proteins. For the latter represents a code and the former does not. Further, there is not the slightest evidence that the grade of coding order resident on a gene could ever be derived from the low-grade order resident on natural catalysts such as clay. It would collide with information theory to hold that high-grade coding or order could be derived spontaneously from lower-grade coding or order, so that the whole idea really founders on theoretical as well as practical considerations. We look into the significance of information theory in this problem later.

Last, there is no evidence that life could subsist on a lower status of sequential coding order than that found in the simplest viruses. Even in these simplest of organisms, the DNA order, followed by the protein sequencing, is such that the lower order of natural catalysts could not, on theoretical grounds, ever give rise to it.

Before concluding this section we must point out that Fox, in pursuing this work on the spontaneous production of proteinoids, went on to produce "microspheres" from his products (see chap. 4) and drew the conclusion that it is possible to proceed from simple gases up to complex microspheres, all by chance reactions. It is enough to mention here that the simplest forms of life, the viruses, contain two main constituents. First, the DNA part containing the genetic code; second, the protein mantle with which the DNA is clothed. But the whole can only be said to live when its coded information can use the cell metabolism of a host organism. Fox's microspheres contain no trace of DNA or a genetic code and therefore cannot seriously be said to be living in any sense of the word.

The same remarks apply to the coacervate work reported by Oparin and others (see chap. 4). The fact remains, that even if we could, by an enormous stretch of the imagination, envisage the spontaneous formation of a DNA molecule and a covering sheath of sequenced protein, we would still not have synthesized life. For such a virus type of complex would still be unable to live unless we could provide it with a complete cell on which it could live as a parasite. Thus, unless life was already present, no virus type of organism could really be said to live.

All these considerations lead us to recognize that there are still huge gaps in the chain of events we might consider as signposts marking the way up to life on a spontaneous naturalistic basis. We have begun, as the result of brilliant scientific research, to be able to read the genetic code, and have found that it resembles the type of code we use in writing. The code is arranged on molecular threads instead of on paper or in sand. Would it not, in the present state of our knowledge, be reasonable to try to make sense of both codes, those on paper and those on molecular threads, by taking them both to be a means of conveying intelligent messages?

Even a code or program fed into a computer is an intelligent message sent from a source of intelligent thought to a machine, which is, of course, a fabrication of human intelligence. Would it not be reasonable to regard a code, such as the genetic code, as *a source of intelligent information sent from a nonhuman intelligence to a biological machine*? The biological machine could, like the computer, be reasonably regarded as a machine made by the same intelligence, the code being the means of communication between the creator intelligence and his creation. There would seem to be nothing intrinsically unreasonable in the suggestion, given the possibility of an intelligence which is the source of the original coding. In a later section we treat further the question of the feasibility of such an extrahuman, nonmaterial intelligence.

One further matter must be touched upon in this section. In the copying of a code, mistakes of a random nature are always likely to occur. These mistakes are of the same random nature as typing errors. Letters are reversed or omitted, destroying the sequence of the code we call writing. It is comparatively easy to correct such purely random mistakes. They are so obviously random errors within meaningful sequences that one can usually recognize them as mistakes.

However, if a manuscript is recopied too often, the random mistakes may become so frequent that passages become incoherent. There are too many random mistakes and too few deliberate sequences in them to make sense.

Our point is that randomness in any code sequence progressively destroys the code. In fact, code sequences and randomness are incompatible. Randomness destroys code, and putting a code onto a randomly arranged thread of biomonomers will destroy randomness. *If randomness and code sequences, then, are so mutually destructive, how can we ever come to the ridiculous conclusion that randomness gave spontaneous birth to code sequences of the super-specificity of the genetic code?* And yet that is, in principle, exactly what some biological scientists are suggesting today. The whole idea is one huge paradox. Code sequences and randomness are as incompatible as fire and water. To maintain that one produced the other spontaneously is about as likely as maintaining that playing an acetylene torch on a pot filled with water causes the water to freeze.

INHERENT MECHANISMS FOR THE PRODUCTION
OF CODING SEQUENCES

Scientists such as Teilhard de Chardin thought that they could account for the coding order and specificity of natural products without any appeal to external help acting on matter. Those who hold with Teilhard—and some who do not—believe that chemical evolution up to life and beyond—to consciousness—is inevitable and is merely a reflection of the "upward psychic urge" resident on the simplest of atoms since their formation millions of years ago. That is, nature automatically tends to life and man and consciousness and "point Omega" (to use Teilhard's own expression) simply because matter is made the way it is. We have looked briefly at this view in discussing Kenyon's Theory of Biochemical Predestination and noted that propounders of that theory hold the same view with the exclusion of the theistic *Weltanschauung*. These ideas really boil down to believing that all nature is an algorithm of, or code for, life, consciousness and point Omega.

It is perhaps fair to state that in recent years such views are coming to be recognized as being in conflict with the second law of thermodynamics which lays down that a fundamental property of matter lies in its innate tendency to disorder and not to codes or order. Unless available energy is applied to overcome the "entropy barrier," no reduction of entropy, or increase in order, can be expected. What Teilhard and his friends are saying is that matter has a fundamental, inherent tendency to increase its order up to life and consciousness. He and many others believe that matter performs this feat at the expense of the second law of thermodynamics by being able to make use of the random energy derived from the sun or from radioactivity. We examine this proposition while dealing with the question of metabolic motors in a later section. For present purposes it is enough to note that there is little evidence that spontaneous radiation such as that from the sun could, without the intermediary of a metabolic motor, account for the hugely reduced entropy status of life as we know it.

However, in spite of the above, it would be incorrect to try to maintain that no order or sequences whatsoever could arise from the built-in properties of the constituent amino acids. It is a fact that varying the side chains present on various reacting amino acids does influence the sequences of amino acid condensation to form polypeptides. Indeed, it would be strange if it did not, for there are quite a number of good theoretical reasons why the varying electron-attracting or electron-repelling properties of various side chains on the different amino acids should interfere with the sequences and even stereospecificity of the compound resulting from apparently random condensation. Many years ago, in fact, this was the subject of a doctor of philosophy thesis I wrote in England, for which I received a doctor's degree.

In dealing with this subject one must, however, distinguish between matters that are different. The sequence differences and variations in specificity and stereochemistry *do not constitute codes* with a specific meaning for specific receptors when they arise due to differences in the electronic nature of side-chain radicals. The biopolymers produced under such differing influences cannot be called *random* polymers. But neither can they be said to contain *coded* information just because they are not random.

AN ILLUSTRATION FROM SPITZBERGEN

An illustration may help us to understand this point better. Some years ago my family and I spent some weeks during the summer in Spitzbergen on the Arctic Ocean. On those beautiful rocky shores we visited a Polish geological expedition which had been doing work on the permafrost there. They were investigating the sometimes complex stone patterns found in these areas. The patterns apparently arise from the expansion and contraction of the rocks during the heating and cooling of day and night, summer and winter. It often looks as though intelligences of some sort had been at work constructing the circles of stones and small crevasses. The Polish scientists assured us, however, that this was not the case and that the patterns were entirely devoid of meaning. That is, there was no code hidden behind them such as one might expect to find behind hieroglyphics.

The nonrandom biopolymers formed as a result of the inherent properties of differing side chains on amino acids are like rings in the permafrost. They are nonrandom, certainly, and yet they possess some sort of sequence or pattern. *But neither the rings in the permafrost nor the proteinoids formed by combining amino acids on natural catalytic surfaces carry, as far as we can establish experimentally, any code or message.* And here is the grand difference between the specific DNA and protein molecules of life, and the proteinoids formed under the influence of nonliving catalysts.

THE MAGNITUDE OF NATURAL SPECIFICITY

If the synthesis of life's protein at the origin of life had been a random event controlled by only the random forces of chemistry, it has been calculated that there would not be enough mass in the entire earth, even though it were composed exclusively of amino acids, to make even one molecule each of all the possible sequences in even a low-weight molecular protein.[1] Inherent properties residing on the amino acids themselves can, and undoubtedly do, give some direction to the synthesis of large protein molecules. Nevertheless it is clear from experiments that such direction as is inherent in the properties of the biomonomers may produce specific patterns but certainly not, in our experience, the patterns of codes.[2]

It would not be in order, however, to make such statements without giving chapter and verse for them! It has been found that alanine is almost twice as likely to couple with a glycine as valine is likely to couple with a glycine residue.[3] Thus, the probability of interaction between any two amino acids depends on:

1. their relative abundance in the reaction mixture
2. their pK values and
3. the physical and chemical properties of the side chains involved.

It must also be remembered that the above type of inherent selectivity is found not only in synthesis but is also met in hydrolysis or decomposition reactions, so that we may conclude that selectivity of this type is a general phenomenon. The phenomenon of selective hydrolysis would help to build up concentrations of specific nonrandom peptides in mixtures because, if hydrolysis is selective in nature, the peptides left behind which were not hydrolyzed will be selected substances too. However, it is the general opinion among scientists working in this field that the phenomenon of selective hydrolysis could not have been a serious factor in the chemical evolution of specificity.[4]

To some scientists these observations prove that specific, viable proteins could have arisen prebiotically without the direction of nucleic acids or even of specific catalysts. The protagonists of the biochemical predestination concept are of this persuasion. Some workers in the area have even gone a step further to maintain that specifically sequenced peptides may have arisen in the above manner prebiotically and then have served as the templates for the information necessary to synthesize DNA molecules later. This would be the exact opposite to that system found in living matter now. For today DNA supplies the information for synthesizing proteins. What is being suggested is that spontaneously formed specific proteins supplied the information for selective DNA synthesis. The evidence for this supposition is, of course, nil.[5]

The important point to remember in all this speculation is that a certain amount of inherent molecular sequencing is certainly possible and is based on sound principles of organic chemistry. But it must be kept firmly in mind that producing sequences of letters in our alphabet of twenty-four letters rather than a purely random higgledy-piggledy arrangement of letters does not, in itself, produce a *code sequence*. Even arranging the letters of the alphabet in patterns, rather than without order, is not to be compared with producing a meaningful code like a Shakespeare sonnet. Order is of two kinds in our present discussion. There is the kind of order which is truly a pattern—like ripples on the seashore—but which bears no code meaning. This order can be compared to letters in an ordered sequence which conveys no particular meaning. Then there is the other kind of sequenced order which hides a meaningful code—like a section of Goethe's poetry. We know of only one way in which the latter can arise and that is by the exercise of intelligence. The first kind can arise either with or without the direct intervention of intelligence.

AUTOCATALYTIC AUTODIRECTIVE FEEDBACK

There is perhaps one other matter we should mention before leaving the subject of sequencing. It is known that the clay Montmorillonite absorbs amino acids and also catalyzes the dimerization of amino acid monomers.[6] This type of catalysis and autocatalysis has led some scientists to believe that the specificity of protein synthesis and the duplication of information storage could have resided in protein structure in the pre- and para-biotic world in the manner we have mentioned above. The polymerization of amino acids to specific peptides and proteins is postulated as being directed by the peptide products themselves in an autocatalytic manner. Thus life is assumed to be a product of autodirective autocatalytic feedback mechanisms working on specific peptide and protein syntheses.

In considering these hypotheses it is of crucial importance to keep in mind two hard facts. First, nature when left to itself with no outside influences, leans to randomizing processes rather than specific ones. This is another way of stating the second law of thermodynamics, and there is no getting around it. Second, life as we know it is uncompromisingly coupled to coding systems of the most complex type. Coding systems have never been known to arise spontaneously out of randomness, but only, in our experience, from motor intelligence. It is, of course, never to be denied, as already emphasized, that some peptide bond specificity will result during spontaneous amino acid condensation and that this specificity will result from the intrinsic properties of the amino acids themselves. But the hard fact remains that we have no experience which would lead us to expect that this type of restraint on random condensations could be *totally* responsible for the arising of the specificity we call a code.

Perhaps a further illustration will pinpoint this matter.

A FURTHER ILLUSTRATION

If one takes suitable metals and machines and fits them together in a certain way it is possible to construct a watch out of them. One has to know something of mathematics as well as metallurgy and watchmakers' skills. Given the metals and their properties, it is possible to impose a certain type of order on the metals which might almost be designated as a kind of mathematical pattern or code.

It would be unacceptable, however, to maintain that the properties of the metals themselves automatically and spontaneously were sufficient to produce the mechanical pattern which is a watch. It is true that one cannot have the watch without the properties of the metals—they are absolutely vital to any watch. But it is equally true that the properties of the metals *alone* (weight, tensile strength, etc.) are insufficient to account for the watch. Random forces might produce all sorts of shapes and patterns with the metals, but the pattern of a watch is inconceivable on the basis of these forces alone. To obtain the watch design—based on the properties of the metals—one has to combine the metals of the watch with the watchmaker's intelligence. There is no other way we know of for producing a watch.

The properties of the elements of which an amino acid is constructed are absolutely vital to life's proteins just as the properties of metals are necessary for a watch—and to a somewhat similar degree. But the properties of the elements of which amino acids are constructed are insufficient to build the coded protein sequences of viable proteins. These properties need to be combined with a coding system to give rise to such a mechanism as constitutes life's proteins. There is no way around the fact that codes derive, sooner or later, from intelligence and thought.

Or look at the problem this way: In Switzerland the Montagnards sometimes obtain building materials from blasting operations. A well-placed charge below an old tree stump can be quite productive in such an operation. A mass of stones possesses certain properties which, when rightly used, can be constructed into a house or a cattle pen. The house or cattle pen construction is dependent on the inherent properties of the stones (their shape, solidity, stability, etc.), but these same inherent properties are insufficient to account for a house. The builder's intelligence is capable of imposing the form or code of a cattle pen or house on these inherent properties, but the latter alone are entirely insufficient to account for the form the house or pen assumes during construction. Blasting operations plus the properties of the stone may produce a crude cave in the mass of building material but never spontaneously give the form of a constructed building. For that is a different type of pattern. In fact, it is also a type of coded pattern.

The type or energy that Miller and others have been feeding into their mixtures of methane, ammonia, steam, etc., is to be compared to the energy fed into a tree stump in blasting operations. It is like lightning or X-radiation. It may produce a mass of building materials or even, under some circumstances, a crude depression or "cave"—a proteinoid. But we cannot—and should not—on theoretical and experimental grounds, expect any code to arise by random mechanisms. They are like fire and water; they do not mix. And yet the life's work of many scientists has been devoted to this attempt—supported by millions of dollars of grants-in-aid. It is folly on theoretical and practical grounds, and flies in the face of all scientific common sense.

We must now look briefly at the principle of the necessity of coding in complex molecular specificity.

COMPLEXITY AND SPECIFICITY

The larger the number of stages leading to an end product in any reaction, the greater the number of chances there are, in general, for formation of undesired by-products. The corollary is also true: The fewer the number of stages leading to an end product, the easier it is to arrive at it without side reactions swamping our flow sheet. This proposition assumes that all energy requirements have been satisfactorily met.

During the formation of simple building blocks or biomonomers there are usually few possible reaction stages. Thus there are fewer side reactions possible than where complex macromolecular synthesis is going on. For the latter are often constructed from tens of thousands of building blocks passing through many stages.

These facts imply that, although simple building blocks can be produced by spontaneous reactions which may be compared to our blasting operations, yet it is difficult to imagine a "house" constructed of tens of thousands of building blocks, and which is the expression of a "code," to be constructed by the same mechanism. The more complex the end product and the more reaction stages leading to it, the greater the necessity of some constraint or "codification" being applied to the system if one specific product is to be obtained.

This "codification" can be applied to a multistaged reaction system requiring specificity in two main ways as we have already pointed out. Either a specific catalyst may be used, or the reaction conditions may be intelligently manipulated so as to favor one specific reaction product at the expense of the undesired ones.

In this connection it has been pointed out by Murray Eden that only a minute portion of the structurally possible protein formulae has been explored by nature. Eden concludes, therefore, that *there must have been a high degree of synthetic direction constraint operative during abiogenesis and vital synthesis following it.* From this fact alone he deduces that protein synthesis, at least, did not originate in spontaneous processes as a result of abiogenetical reactions.[7] The same argument, of course, applies to the super-specificity known as optical activity in living molecules. We have already endeavored to show that the specificity derived from natural catalysts is insufficient to account for the type of natural specificity observed in living material.

Accordingly, Eden believes that some very active form of synthesis (or degradative) constraint must have been operative from abiogenesis onward.

We look at a few more aspects of multistage reactions and specificity in a later chapter.

1. G. Steinman, *Arch. Biochem. Biophys.* 119 (1967): 76; and 121 (1967): 533.

2. S. W. Fox, K. Harada, K. R. Woods and C. R. Windsor, *Arch. Biochem. Biophys.* 102 (1963): 439; and G. Krampitz, *Naturwiss* 46 (1959): 558.

3. Dean H. Kenyon and M. V. Cole, *Proc. Natl. Acad. Sc.* 58 (1967): 735.

4. Kenyon and Steinman, *Biochemical Predestination,* p. 211.

5. J. Lederberg, *Science* 131 (1966): 269.

6. Steinman, *Arch. Biochem. Biophys.* 121 (1967): 533.

7. Murray Eden, article in P. S. Moorhead and M. M. Kaplan, eds., in *Mathematical Challenges to the Neo-Darwinian Interpretation of Evolution,* p. 7.

4.

prebiological systems

THE IMPORTANCE OF UNDERSTANDING ORIGINS

We have now glanced at some of the theories concerned with prebiotic chemical evolution, processes believed by many protobiologists to have taken place during some two or more billion years.[1] We must now turn our attention to some different aspects of this same problem of prebiotic chemical evolution. It is generally recognized today that the greatest problem of past biotic history lies with the question of organizing matter without the help of living material up to a state capable of bearing life.

A. I. Oparin, speaking at a conference on prebiotic evolution held at Wakulla Springs, Florida, on October 27-30, 1963, opened his remarks as follows:

> Heracleitus was the first, with Aristotle following him, who understood that to know the nature of things you have to know their origins. These profound words, of course, apply to the nature of life, which can also be understood only in the light of its origin.[2]

Presumably the corollary to this statement also applies—
that if we are hazy about the origin of life, we shall be hazy
about its nature and meaning. Perhaps we could risk taking
the further step of logic by maintaining that if we know
nothing about the origin of life at all, we shall also ipso facto
know nothing of its meaning.

It is obvious that we can only speculate inductively on the
origins of prebiological chemical and metabolic systems. But
would it not be better to refrain from speculating at all if our
guesses are of the kind which some protobiologists offer us?
Oparin, for example, uses phrases and words on this subject
which are almost meaningless when examined closely. But
they *look* deeply meaningful to the uninitiated. One example:

> This is how the gradual perfection of both the living system
> as a whole and of its individual mechanisms proceeded.
> Proteins-enzymes and the nucleic acids related to their
> synthesis, *adapted themselves* ever better to performance of
> their biological functions, the selection of these compounds
> being a function of the strictly definite arrangement of
> monomers in the polynucleotide chains—what was an indis-
> pensable condition for the constancy of enzyme syntheses
> in growing and reproducing systems.[3]

Could one wish for a more complete example of begging
the question? For what we really need to know is exactly
how proteins adapted themselves and *how* they learned to
perform their biological functions better. Not only is the
question thoroughly begged, it is begged in the sort of superb
gobbledygook which will impress the uninitiated so that he
will be blind to the need to sort out the real meaning behind
the statement. We are vitally interested in knowing just how
the selection of the required compounds came to be a "function of the strictly definite arrangement of monomers in their
polynucleotide chains"—especially if the basis of everything
biological is originally random. For randomness must have
been the original governing law of life if the Neo-Darwinian

views are correct, as Oparin believes them to be. The term "gradual perfection" cannot be used to sweep the whole problem under the carpet, nor can "definite arrangement" be used to replace expressions such as "random arrangement" without some qualifying explanation of the process by which the change occurred.

COACERVATES

Oparin then goes on to elaborate his ideas on coacervates as steps in the process of "gradual perfection" toward "definite arrangements."[4] Before examining his ideas on this subject, an exact description of coacervates is necessary, for there is a good deal of confusion on the subject.

Coacervate formation has been observed in solutions of large molecules in water. Coacervates consist of spheres or droplets surrounded by a kind of "cell wall" separating the contents from the surrounding solution. These droplets or coacervates tend to be unstable and, although they may show some structure, there is nothing in them comparable to the inner structure of a living cell.

Microspheres have been observed to be formed under somewhat different conditions and have also been proposed as forerunners of living entities on the prebiological earth.[5] Although Oparin and others suggest both coacervate and microsphere formation as a stepping-stone up to life, exact details of how this might be the case have been withheld. When details of this transference of a microsphere or coacervate to a living entity are requested, refuge is usually taken in bons mots such as: "A billion years are needed in order to realize that."[6]

Statements like this mean that evolution up to life via coacervate or microsphere formation would be easily feasible if one merely adds a billion years to the equation we are trying to solve. Of course, one might just as well maintain that the Golden Gate Bridge would arise spontaneously if one just gave the iron ore of which it is constructed a billion years or so to organize itself.

Coacervates are believed to be the end product of the reduction of the hydration layer surrounding colloidal particles.[7] By mutual exclusion of water, a number of particles unite to produce an oily droplet in the form of a coacervate. This means really that any agent tending to promote dehydration in aqueous solutions of large molecules containing hydrophobic side chains will usually encourage coacervate formation. Thus any molecules which are very soluble in water will tend to produce coacervates when added to aqueous solutions of substance containing fat-soluble side chains.

Biochemists and others will recognize that the principles of coacervate formation are related to those of the process known as "salting out." Coacervate formation using potassium oleate solution in water to which potassium chloride is added demonstrates this. For example, potassium oleate consists of a highly soluble potassium ion together with a much less water-soluble oleate moiety (chemical part). If increasing amounts of potassium chloride are added to a fairly concentrated solution of potassium oleate in water, two phases (or layers) will eventually be formed in the place of the original layer. An upper oily layer separates from the lower or aqueous layer. Just at the beginning of this separation process oily droplets will appear which are called coacervates.

This "salting-out process" is explained by assuming that the potassium chloride competes for the water molecules in the potassium oleate solution, thus separating the water molecules from the long fatty oleate chains which are hydrophobic in any case. The latter therefore separate from the aqueous phase as soon as sufficient water has been withdrawn by the competition by the potassium chloride ions. The potassium oleate molecules therefore eventually separate from the water when sufficient water has been withdrawn by the potassium chloride, and they appear as oily droplets or coacervates, which are spherical micelles.

Coacervation based on similar principles can be observed using proteins in aqueous solutions. Complex coacervates can be formed between gelatin and gum arabic by making use of exactly the same principles. Basic proteins such as histone, and acidic substances such as nucleic acid may also be induced to undergo coacervate associations. Coacervates may be formed from diluted or concentrated solutions, according to the solubility relationships in water of the compounds used.

The important point to understand is the use to which this well-known phenomenon is put by scientists of Oparin and Kenyon's persuasion. Kenyon may be taken as an example here, for he expresses himself perfectly clearly as follows:

> It has been proposed that the phenomenon of coacervation could have served as a primitive protocell-forming mechanism. With the realization that salts were undoubtedly present in the primitive bodies of water and the suggestion that appropriate coacervate-forming large molecules could have been synthesized by this stage of evolution, the possible role of primordial coacervates in the appearance of protocells has been investigated in detail. This phenomenon would provide a means for the establishment of bounded internal environments for the localized development of protometabolic reaction sequences.

The language sounds impressive but the data on which it is founded are shaky. The argument runs thus: Coacervate formation accounts for the spontaneous formation of boundaries separating an internal cell environment from an external one. This represents a first and very basic requirement for the formation and maintenance of life's metabolism. In the huge dilutions of the ocean, the concentration of metabolizing substances would be insufficient to support metabolism. The substances *must be concentrated and maintained at optimal concentrations*. This restraining function is carried out by a cell membrane which is therefore mandatory for any form of life.

Assuming that a buildup of salts in solution did take place in the primordial oceans, and that complex organic polymers were already present by the action of chemical evolution in

such a primordial sea, we should expect salting-out or coacervate formation to take place. Oily droplets would be formed.
However, these are not stable except under very carefully
defined conditions. The pH value (acidity) must be correct.
Violent disturbances must not occur or the droplets will be
destroyed. We know that anything but the mildest of centrifugation will result in their destruction. For they coalesce
under such circumstances to form a continuous oily layer just
as one would expect. This means that the boundary is somewhat unstable and lacks the regular properties of a biological
cell boundary.

However, unstable as they are, we now have the coacervate
droplets on our hands for investigation as candidates for the
ambitious title of "protocells." Kenyon characterizes his
coacervates in some detail. He finds, for example, that the
droplets can take in and "utilize" materials from their environment. They absorb organic materials from their environment so that "their mass increases."

How this process of increasing mass by taking in materials
from the environment can be anything but trivial does not
appear from the text. For a blotter will also, surprisingly
enough, take up ink from its environment with a corresponding "increase in mass"! Surely it does not need special
experimentation to show that oily droplets of any substance
of the type used for these tests will dissolve any suitable
organic substances which happen to be near them! It is not
exactly a matter for writing home about (or even noting in
textbooks on protobiology) that thereby the mass of such
droplets will be increased.

The vital point for us in this whole matter is whether, by
means of coacervate formation, we have found any parallel or
even insight into biological cell formation, or into the mechanism by which cells increase their mass. That is, whether
coacervate formation gives us insight into abiogenesis or into
cell metabolism resulting in growth. It is our view that there
is absolutely no parallel in the formation of coacervates and
protocells. We risk this rather categorical statement on the

grounds that there is no evidence that salting-out processes could ever produce anything resembling the inner structure of the true biological cell. *For the true biological cell is always, in our experience, so structured and complex that it may be classed as almost one large code in its sequences and specificity. On theoretical grounds alone we do not see any possibility of such structures arising by mere salting-out mechanisms.*

A second reason for not accepting the parallel nature of coacervate formation and protocell formation is provided by the solid fact that there is no real analogy between mere increase in mass (growth by simple physical absorption on the blotter) and increase in size and mass by means of metabolic processes or biochemical transformation. It is obvious that coacervate mass increase does not occur by metabolic processes but by purely physical absorption.

Purely superficial resemblances are being dressed up to resemble cell processes where no fundamental resemblances exist. In fact, some of the citations given to support the coacervate-protocell type of theory resemble pure propaganda in support of the scientific materialistic view of life. In reality, any fundamental likenesses between even the simplest living cells and coacervates are conspicuous by their absence.

This same type of superficiality of thought characterizes the reports that enzymes (for example, catalase) are "taken up" by coacervates which then, staggeringly enough, proceed to show catalase activity.[9] Surely if one dissolves any catalyst or enzyme in a solvent, or even absorbs it on a sponge, that solvent or sponge will show the activity of the catalyst or enzyme now present in it! Even if one dissolves hydrogen peroxide in water, the resulting aqueous solution will show hydrogen peroxide activity. Catalase, when in an aqueous medium or when absorbed onto an oily drop, will show its properties! The remarkable thing is that there has been no protest over this sort of travesty of scientific seriousness. Perhaps the reason is that so many actively wish to be fed with diluted intellectual soup of this kind.

Even after reporting all these "likenesses" between coacervates and protocell formation, Kenyon himself does not seem, in his heart of hearts, to be very convinced by his own efforts. For after trying to establish his theories in the above reported manner, he confesses at the end of it all, "It is important to emphasize at this point that coacervation is not necessarily taken here to be the one and only phenomenon behind protocell development." [10] And again: "Although coacervates in particular display many interesting properties shared with living cells, the exact means of internal differentiation to specific cellular inclusions is unclear. . . . " And, *"No coacervate has yet been reported which shows in its boundaries the structural regularity found in living cells."* [11]

Here, at last, we have something less trivial! For the structural regularity found in living cells is a vastly important criterion. Coacervates have never shown this type of inner-structural regularity. The spontaneous appearance of morphogenicity (body or structure formation) which Kenyon goes to extreme lengths to prove, has never shown such regularity. For that type of regular pattern which characterizes the living cell arises not as a result of the principle of morphogenicity but as the result of the outworking of a most sophisticated *coding arrangement* on the genes of life. Codes do not arise, as far as we are aware, by any spontaneous morphogenicity.

MICROSPHERES

The term "microsphere" in some books on protobiology is often referred to under a so-called synonym, namely, "protocell." This rather ambitious term is used to describe the formation of small, roundish bodies under a variety of chemical conditions. Microspheres may resemble coacervates, but in some ways they differ. For instance, they are stable enough to be separated from the medium in which they were formed. Mild centrifugation is often effective. Kenyon and Steinman publish photographs of these bodies, which in their rounded shapes superficially resemble biological cells.

When simple mixtures of ammonia, hydrogen and water are subjected to electron bombardment, microsphere formation has been observed. Microspheres are small, spherical bodies of solid material formed when various simple mixtures are sparked together or otherwise supplied with energy. Their size varies, as does their chemical constitution.[12] In general I believe it is fair to state that the chemical analysis of microspheres shows little relevance to the chemical analysis of living organisms. For further information on this subject, reference may be made to Kenyon and Steinman's book cited.

By sparking ammonia, hydrogen and water together, microspheres were obtained which contained a large amount of inorganic material, possibly silicates, extracted from the borosilicate glass of the sparking apparatus when exposed to ammonia. Some amino acids were also found in the spherules. This means that the chemical nature of these microspheres was heterogeneous and, to some extent, fortuitous, being influenced by the constitution of the glass apparatus in which the experiment was conducted. However, no trace of metabolism or of viable protein formation was observed in the microspheres described by Kenyon and others.

COACERVATES, MICROSPHERES AND MORPHOGENICITY

Kenyon and Steinman use the facts of the spontaneous formation (morphogenicity) of coacervates and microspheres to bolster up their theory of biochemical predestination. These authors believe that, just as biomonomers are formed spontaneously from their component elements, so protocells or cells are formed spontaneously from biopolymers. Elements combine spontaneously to form building blocks or biomonomers. What could be more natural than to suppose that building blocks in their turn combine with one another spontaneously to form protocells, and then cells?

This supposed tendency of building blocks to combine to form protocells, coacervates or microspheres is known as morphogenicity and is observed when ordered, cell-like bodies (coacervates, microspheres) arise from biomonomers spontaneously. In fact, Kenyon and Steinman use coacervate and microsphere formation to "prove" the reality of morphogenicity. The argument goes like this: If coacervates and microspheres resemble cells, and if coacervates and microspheres arise spontaneously, could not complete, functioning cells also have arisen from biomonomers spontaneously? The whole logic of Kenyon and Steinman's argument turns on the point that coacervates and microspheres compare with biological cells in structure and function. And if the two entities, microspheres and coacervates, really have nothing to do with cells and their complex structure, then Kenyon and Steinman are barking up the wrong tree.

It is our firm conviction that the type of morphogenicity used to describe the formation of coacervates and microspheres has little to do with the type of morphogenicity which would describe the formation of a living cell. The two processes are as different as chalk is from cheese.

Before we can go into the reasons for this conclusion we shall have to look into the criteria which Kenyon and others use for deciding whether a structure is alive or not, for a good deal of Kenyon's argument turns just on this point. He attempts to show that coacervates and microspheres possess many of the attributes of living cells, and therefore he assumes that they are signposts on the way up to life. One has the feeling that if one could only wait a little longer, Kenyon's morphogenicity would produce the full-blown living cell! We wish to show that coacervates and microspheres have no significant attributes of life and cannot therefore be considered in any way as being signposts leading up to living organisms.

CRITERIA OF "BEING ALIVE"

In discussions such as this it is very important to be able to define exactly the criteria of *being alive*. We must be able to decide on what basis an aggregate of matter merits the designation "living matter." This is by no means easy, for there is no single criterion which can be used. We are forced to use a number of criteria and then to use the sum of them in deciding whether, on the whole, a particular unit of matter is alive.

Some of the phenomena exhibited by a living cell are: a living cell ingests, metabolizes, digests, provides energy for itself, absorbs, secretes, reacts to external stimuli, reproduces and excretes. Any one unit of life may not necessarily show all these properties at once. For example, a mule is certainly alive, but it cannot reproduce. A castrate cannot reproduce either, but is certainly alive. An enucleated amoeba cell continues to carry out some metabolism but cannot reproduce itself. A person under deep general anesthesia does not react to external stimuli, but is certainly alive. Secretion by certain organs of the human body may be suspended during extreme stress, but the person is certainly still alive. It is obvious, then, that we shall have to sum up the properties of a given aggregate of matter in order to decide if, on the whole, we can consider it to be alive.

Kenyon and Steinman take the above criteria of "being alive" and apply them to the properties of their microspheres. As a result they conclude that microspheres are a true form of a "sub-life" and are therefore signposts pointing to the mechanism of the formation of true life. Their reasons are: microspheres have been observed to show processes resembling "growth," "budding," "ingestion," "vocuolation," and even "excretion." [13] They therefore compare these properties with those shown by biological cells and consider them to be comparable. Thus, in their eyes, morphogenicity is proved and the microsphere is a protocell which has arisen spontaneously. It is as easy as that. But we must evaluate their evidence.

Take, for example, Kenyon's belief that ingestion as shown by microspheres parallels ingestion by biological cells. As already pointed out, ingestion in the living cell is a complex enzymatic process involving various reaction stages and chains. In the microsphere there is no evidence that any enzymes are present at all, so that an enzymatic process is out of the question in explaining microsphere ingestion. There is every evidence that the latter is a purely mechanical or physical phenomenon, while biological cell ingestion is a highly chemical process. Thus there is little parallel between the ingestive processes in a microsphere and those in the cell.

Next, we may look at the process of budding and reproduction. In the microsphere, budding of a "physical" type certainly does take place. But it is quite different from cell division which is controlled by a complex process involving strands of chromosomes and genes which split down the middle so as to assure each new bud an equal portion of the genetic material of the original cell. The various phases of this complex process in the dividing cell have been observed and photographed for years. The mechanism by which a DNA strand divides has been closely studied. The whole process of reproduction is dependent on strand-splitting, and without it no real passing on of heredity would be possible. Surely, in view of these well-known processes behind cell reproduction and "budding," it is a mystery that any scientist could imagine that budding in microspheres shows any parallels at all with biological reproduction. For microspheres do not contain any DNA strands or genes to work on!

The same considerations apply to the process of "growth." The living cell grows by means of ingestion followed by chemical transformation or metabolism based on complex enzyme systems. The increase in mass and size of a cell is thus a highly complex chemical and enzymatic process. The microsphere, however, does not contain any enzymes by which chemical growth could take place. It grows by physical absorption in the same way that the oil volume in the crankcase of your car may grow if too much cheap gasoline leaks past the pistons, descends into the crankcase, dissolves in the lubricating oil, and thus increases the volume of the oil. Few scientists (or laymen for that matter) would seriously liken the growth in volume of crankcase oil with the growth of an amoeba.

Thus we conclude that microspheres and coacervates possess only a superficial resemblance to biological cells. Their chemical composition is different. Unlike biological cells, they contain no specific viable protein sequences, nor do they contain any genetic mechanism such as that of DNA or RNA which are absolute necessities of life as we know it. The very fact that biological cells are highly *coded*, while microspheres and coacervates are not, should help us to distinguish that which is different.

Having now tried to establish the pith of the matter from theoretical and practical considerations, we cannot leave this problem without indicating some of the extremes to which the subject has been pushed.

FURTHER EVIDENCE CITED BY KENYON AND STEINMAN

Aldehydes and nitriles combine in spark-discharge synthesis to yield products considered by Kenyon and others to have potential significance in explaining the appearance of primordial biological cells. Not only have spark-discharge experiments been used to support Kenyon's line of thought, but "wet reactions" have been pulled into the line of battle in the same interest.

When ammonium thiocyanate was dissolved in formaldehyde solution and then spread in thin layers on a surface and incubated for several hours, "active microscopic structures resembling living cells appeared."[14] Kenyon describes this phenomenon in some detail and reports that "this morphogenetic experiment was repeated many times and resulted in a large variety of forms bearing a strong resemblance to living cells. They included such things as internal movement, vacuole exclusion and translocation."[15] Here we have several similarities between the living cell and the products of reaction microspheres between ammonium thiocyanate and formaldehyde. Because of these similarities this phenomenon was given the name "plasmogeny" (or genesis of protoplasm)!

Work of this type was continued, using various reaction conditions, with the result that "the formation of microspheres was found to be enhanced by ultraviolet radiation ... the incorporation of zinc into the formaldehyde-thiocyanate structures led to a localized ATP-ase-like activity."[16] ATP-ase activity is, of course, an enzyme activity found in living cells, so that Kenyon concludes that he has found yet another similarity to life in his formaldehyde thiocyanate microspheres.

With all due deference to the opinions of mature scientists, we find it difficult to accept this kind of evidence for any sort of real, relevant, genuine protocell formation. Nothing would need to be said about it if it were merely a private opinion of respected scientists. The rub comes when observations of this kind are seriously put before immature students as proof for the scientific materialistic view of life in general. However, when propaganda for an atheistic *Weltanschauung* based on observations of this type is propounded, something must be done to expose the view for what it is, even though the attempt may make an unfortunately critical impression. Let us therefore spend a moment or two on the examination of the claims of "plasmogeny," or the artificial generation of the "plasma of life."

In the first place, formaldehyde and thiocyanate solutions do not produce substances showing chemical compositions in any way connected with those exhibited by living protoplasm. In the complex substances produced by reacting formaldehyde with thiocyanate there can be no trace of a genetic mechanism such as DNA or RNA molecules, nor is there any sign of optical activity or sequenced, specific proteins. All these fundamental matters *common to all life as we know it* are entirely lacking in Kenyon and others' plasmogeny. Any organic chemist will recognize at once, from an inspection of the reaction, that even as fundamental a property of life's molecules as optical activity cannot, on theoretical grounds, be squarely represented in the products of Kenyon's plasmogeny as he describes it. To obtain molecular asymmetry from optically inactive substances such as formaldehyde and thiocyanate is just impossible without some very involved chemical manipulation and optical resolution processes using optically active molecules of a quite complex nature. No life has ever been discovered which is devoid of optical activity in its molecules. DNA and RNA molecules together with coded, sequenced, specific proteins are also mandatory. These are the barest minima which are associated with the material structure of living organisms. Yet Kenyon's microspheres can, on theoretical grounds, show none of them, arising as they do from the spontaneous reaction of formaldehyde and thiocyanate. If Kenyon had found such properties we may be quite sure he would have reported them. Silence on these points shows their absence and this silence is confirmed on theoretical grounds.

Leaving the purely physical properties of Kenyon's microspheres, which we have already mentioned, we are forced to the conclusion that chemically, at least, they have *nothing* in common with the structural basis of living matter. A freshman taking organic chemistry would see that no DNA, RNA, sequenced protein coding nor optical activity could, on principle, be present in Kenyon's products and that therefore, to chemically compare life's products with them is like comparing worms with windmills. Surely the purely physical properties described, such as vacuolization, internal movement and translocation, would not lead anyone to the unwarranted conclusions drawn. One might as well conclude that the physical principles on which toothpaste is extruded from a tube are intrinsically and phylogenetically related to the evolution of the mammalian defecation process! To be sure, the principles are similar, just as the translocation of the living cell and that of the microsphere are similar, but the derivation of the mechanisms is an entirely different matter.

The next step that scientific materialists take is even more remarkable. It amounts to proposing that, because the outward shape of their microspheres resembles that of a biological cell, the derivation of the two structures is related. In fact, Kenyon boldly labels microspheres as protocells on this basis. In science it is the *inward* morphology and structure that counts, not the outward frame. Yet, on the basis of internal movement, vacuole exclusions and translocation—possibly due to concentration changes in the medium or to some other simple cause—the new word "plasmogeny" has been coined.[17] Would it not be as reasonable to compare a synthetic sponge and its development with a living natural one and its development? Outwardly the two may be similar and functionally alike, but surely the comparison ends there.

Although all the above properties of the "protocells" are described in detail, the most basic and important property, their chemical constitution, is entirely neglected. In fact, one of the highlights of the work is reached with the following announcement on microspheres: "The exact chemical nature of the macromolecules produced by this method was not definitely established."[18] Yet, in the absence of this absolutely fundamental piece of information, we are seriously asked to believe that the experiment throws light on the origin of life. Surely if life is a purely chemical phenomenon (which the scientific materialists would have us believe), are we not at least entitled to information on the chemical constitution of a complex which is alleged to throw light on the origin of the chemical phenomenon of life? Sir Peter Medawar has rightly classified better work than this as "pious bunk."

As already mentioned, the significance of microspheres is not to be judged merely on the basis of their outward form or shape but rather on the basis of their inward structure and composition, particularly their chemical constitution and structure. When we realize the scanty information with which we are supplied on chemical matters, the doubtful foundation on which this particular protobiological house rests becomes even more obvious. For we learn that even though amino acids have been found in some species of microspheres, they are not even linked to one another by peptide bonds. They showed a negative biuret reaction, trypsin incubation was ineffective, and the characteristic infrared spectral bands were lacking.[19] Yet, in spite of the negative nature of all these crucial tests, photographs of the "cell membranes" of these microspheres have been published to demonstrate to the unwary how similar they are to living cell membranes.

Photographic evidence has also been published to show how some species of microspheres "bud" (that is, "reproduce"), how their size increases, and what is the influence of light and radiation on growth. Information on their pyrophosphatase activity is also given. In fact, the enthusiasm for the spherical structures of unknown chemical constitution, and which lack peptide bond properties, is so great that a new name was coined especially for them. It is "Jeewanu," a Sanskrit word meaning "particles of life"![20]

The amount of toil put into this kind of scientific effort is enormous. It shows what importance is attached to the naturalistic rather than the supernaturalistic origin of life. One or two more experiments must be reported on to show how no stone is left unturned in this quest. Aqueous dilute solutions of molybdic acid, paraformaldehyde and ferric chloride were exposed to bright sunlight. A species of microsphere was produced thus in the course of time.[21] The use of molybdate in the experiment was suggested by the role that this radical plays in plant biochemistry. After six hundred hours' exposure to bright sunlight the solutions became turbid. Microscopic examination revealed the presence of microspheres of 1.28 to 0.5μ in diameter. They were mobile, exhibited an external membranelike structure and had a dark interior. No such microspheres appeared in solutions left in the dark.

In solutions irradiated for a thousand hours the resulting spheres increased to 1 to 1.5μ in diameter and developed structures resembling buds. Photographs of these structures are given. Hydrolysis of the product indicated the presence of amino acids. It was found that the constitution of the interior of the spheres differed from that of the external substrate, indicating that a membrane was present capable of delimiting the chemical boundaries of the microsphere. The products would not grow on bacterial nutrient media and, as far as one could ascertain, no bacterial contamination was present which could have accounted for the properties of the microspheres observed. The experiment was carried out under aseptic conditions to guard against this contingency. Few serious scientists would concede that experiments of this type, involving molybdic acid, are relevant to life as we know it, riding as it does on carbon compounds.

Other types of microspheres have been reported on. There are those which result from the autocatalytic production of copper oxide from Fehling's solution in the presence of sugar. [22] Such a process yields spheres even without irradiation. By utilizing the seeding method, the size and number of the microspheres were increased. Buds appeared and multiplication was established. Addition of ammonium molybdate to the reaction mixture resulted in enhanced budding, as did also the presence of gum-arabic sucrose mixtures. When salts were added to the mixtures the inherent movements of the spheres and their growth increased!

In experiments of the above type the microspheres are produced by the well-known Fehling reaction and they consist of small particles of copper oxide. In spite of the rather voluminous literature on Fehling's reaction, Bahadur, who performed these experiments on microspheres, did take the precaution of carrying out a chemical analysis. He reports, not unexpectedly, the following chemical analysis: copper, 48.8 percent; carbon, 4.2 percent; and nitrogen, 0.3 percent.

From the above analysis it is obvious that the microspheres consist of a preponderant amount of copper, probably copper oxide, seeing they are the result of Fehling's reaction. In the absence of a total analysis, one would guess that the compound is not pure but is contaminated with sugars and nitrogenous compounds from the substrate.

After the announcement of the analysis, a piece of really superb showmanship is laid out to catch the feet of the unwary. It is reported with all due solemnity that the "CuO spherules demonstrated a localized catalase-like activity by their ability to accelerate the breakdown of hydrogen peroxide. *A product of moderate dimensions was indicated by the fact that such activity dialyzed very slowly.*"[23]

Kenyon is here trying to lead his readers to believe in the presence of a type of catalase activity which resides on a large molecule—just as in life. In fact, the alleged molecule is so large that it passes through a semipermeable membrane very slowly. This obviously is assumed to look like the catalase activity of life itself. Actually the observation amounts to an almost incredible piece of either showmanship or—to put the worst interpretation upon it, which one is unwilling to do— ignorance. Any chemist who knows his chemistry realizes that the reduction products of Fehling's solution contain heavy metals and that heavy metals, including copper, possess in themselves the faculty of decomposing hydrogen peroxide, that is, catalase activity! No wonder then that this famous "catalase activity" would diffuse out through a semipermeable membrane so slowly! Copper and copper oxide particles do not pass such membranes well! But they do exhibit "catalase activity" in decomposing hydrogen peroxide solutions—a fact which engineers handling concentrated hydrogen peroxide have to keep well in mind in their designing operations!

To assign relevancy to the origin of life on account of the occurrence of "catalase-like activity" in the products of Fehling's solution sounds very much like a covert attempt to pull wool over the eyes of the unwary and the unknowledgeable in the interests of scientific materialism. One would hardly dare to impute ignorance of the facts of copper and catalase activity to such well-known and reputable scientists.

REDUCTIO AD ABSURDUM

Kenyon and Steinman report other, and unfortunately similar, experiments with the same end in view, namely, that of proving that morphogenicity is an inherent property of simple chemical biomonomers and other substances and that this morphogenicity is relevant to the problem of the origin of life on the earth. It is on the basis of work such as we have briefly reported that Kenyon propounds his theory of biochemical predestination.[24]

The present author, after having worked through the evidence presented by Kenyon claiming to show that morphogenicity relevant to neobiogenesis has been demonstrated, has come to the conclusion that the evidence produced is without significance. The growth, budding, vacuolization, surface membranes, internal translocation and spherical morphology observed in microspheres show about as much relevancy to life's processes as the growth, budding, vacuolization, surface membranes, internal translocation and spherical morphology of soap bubbles on the lathered face of the shaver show to problems of the origin of life. For a good many soap bubbles, when observed attentively, show similar phenomena of growth, translocation, surface membranes, and budding together with a beautiful spherical morphology; even the internal contents look dark when viewed under the correct lighting conditions. Some expert soap-bubble blowers (I learned this when my eldest son was still very small) demonstrate excellent soap-bubble budding, given the right sort of pipe and detergent solution.

If the above class of evidence is the best the scientific materialist can put forward to support his naturalistic view of life and its origin, then the scientist who believes in the supernatural origin of the order known as life has nothing whatsoever to fear from intellectual scientific materialism.

AN ILLUSTRATION FROM TURKEY

We may be allowed, perhaps, to sum up these rather lengthy descriptions of laboratory experiments and their meaning with an illustration which may clarify these technical matters a little more.

It has been my privilege and pleasure to have lived for some time in Turkey, helping with the development of Hacettepe University in Ankara. As a result of the initiative of a Turkish pediatrician, a vast institute of higher learning has been produced from scratch in a matter of a few years. Already some five thousand students are studying under its aegis. Most of the main disciplines are offered and professors from the United States, Russia, France, England and Germany are members of its faculty.

Basically, for most of this progress in higher learning, as well as in statecraft, modern Turkey has one man to thank: Kemal Atatürk, affectionately called the "Father of the Turks." It is therefore understandable that all over Turkey are found pictures and equestrian statues commemorating this great man. One can scarcely enter any building or shop without being confronted with the likeness of the "Father of Modern Turkey" looking at one with his penetrating blue eyes. The ubiquitous likenesses are to be found not only all over Ankara, Istanbul, Izmir and Kayseri, the larger cities in Turkey, but even in the smallest villages.

Would it not, however, be incredible to expect even the most backward Turk (Turkey is doing all it can to eliminate illiteracy from its borders, but the rate is still, in some parts, as high as 40 percent, I understand), to believe that the outward likeness of Kemal Atatürk, which he reveres, hides the actual inward morphology of the fatal cirrhotic liver which ended his career in an untimely manner? To go one stage further, would even the simplest Eastern Turkish nomad be caught believing that the steed on which Atatürk is riding in his equestrian statues is related to a living, full-blooded Arab?

And yet, if we call a spade a spade, this is something like what the propagators of the theory of biological predestination are asking us to do. For they expect to be able to prove to us that morphogenicity is a fact by showing that microspheres and coacervates possess some superficial morphological likenesses to biological cells. The likeness of Atatürk does not possess the fatal cirrhotic liver nor does Arabian blood pulse through the equestrian statue.

One is almost ashamed to write this. It is too naïve. Yet, under cover of high-sounding scientific language, we are asked to believe that microspheres *are* protocells, when they are, in reality, merely "statues" or outward likenesses, possessing *nothing of the inward morphology* of the true cell.

The fact remains, therefore, that the *old theory* that life arose by accident falls down on the fact that long time spans do not allow the second law of thermodynamics to be contravened, for long time spans tend to equilibrium and not to the lowering of entropy unless metabolic motors are present. And now the *new theory*, that life did not arise by accident but by the outworking of the inherent, innate properties of matter, so that life is inevitable if matter is left to itself under the correct conditions, collapses on the grounds we have described above. For the law of morphogenicity is no law as far as life's inner morphology is concerned. An invalid proposition or a "no law" certainly does not support the proposed theory of biological predestination.

This all means that the scientific materialists still have no explanation which can be scientifically validated to support their contention that life arose on a purely materialistic non-supernatural basis. Later we examine the scientific basis on which Christians and other believers in God as the Creator of life, as well as matter, can scientifically validate their beliefs.

1. Dean H. Kenyon and Gary Steinman, *Biochemical Predestination,* p. 218.

2. A. I. Oparin, article in S. W. Fox, ed., *The Origins of Prebiological Systems,* p. 91.

3. Ibid., p. 341.

4. Ibid., pp. 331-34.

5. Richard S. Young, article in *The Origins . . . ,* pp. 347-57.

6. Oparin, p. 345.

7. Kenyon and Steinman, p. 245.

8. Ibid., p. 246.

9. Ibid., p. 248.

10. Ibid., p. 249.

11. Ibid., p. 251.

12. K. A. Grossenbacher and C. A. Knight, article in *The Origins . . . ,* pp. 173-86.

13. Kenyon and Steinman, p. 239.

14. A. L. Herrara, *Science* 96 (1942): 14.

15. Kenyon and Steinman, p. 236.

16. Ibid. and A. E. Smith, J. J. Silver and Gary Steinman, *Experientia* 24 (1969): 36.

17. Kenyon and Steinman, p. 236.

18. Ibid.
19. Ibid., p. 237.
20. Ibid., pp. 238, 254; and K. Bahadur, *Synthesis of Jeewanu, the Protocell.*
21. Kenyon and Steinman, p. 238.
22. Ibid., p. 239.
23. Ibid.
24. Ibid., pp. 239-87.

5.

the genetic code and its meaning

We have spent some time looking at the problem of morphogenicity in its relationship to biochemical predestination and have endeavored to show that the whole attempt to prove that morphogenicity is relevant to abiogenesis founders on the fact that the examples of morphogenicity cited are merely instances of superficial resemblances rather than fundamental likenesses. One of the fundamental structures lacking in microspheres and coacervates is the basis of a genetic code which is so essential for all life as we know it today. For us to treat the problem of the origin and meaning of life we must examine the genetic code and its meaning.

RANDOM PROCESSES IN ARCHEBIOPOESIS

In order to set up any code, order must be imposed on the symbols used to bear the code. In other words, randomness has to be replaced by sequences in the "alphabet" on which the code is carried. We must examine briefly the methods available for extracting order from randomness in this context.

At this point a basic hiatus exists in much of the thinking expressed by protobiologists. Oparin's writings, among many others, display a failure to take into account the thermodynamic processes necessary for the ordering of matter up to a state of complexity capable not only of bearing life but also of passing on this complexity to future generations by reproduction. It is for this reason that, without such code systems, no microsphere could truly be said to live or to reproduce. Code systems are vital for both.

It is obvious, therefore, that to understand life's origin it is necessary to understand the origin of coding systems and codes. This, in turn, is basically an aspect of extracting order and sequences from chaotic or random arrangements of matter. It is the failure to take this coding aspect of life, its structure and maintenance, into account which allows Kenyon and his friends to imagine that randomness and spontaneity could produce a microsphere which really resembles life—or to imagine that they have produced a "protocell." The essential structures of life, materially viewed, are codes, and these are lacking in microspheres.

For our purposes the fundamental nature of a code consists in the assigning of certain meanings, which may be concrete or abstract, to a set of sequence symbols. Thus, in a watch, distances traversed by certain notches on wheels represent the passage of certain segments of time. Distances between cogs on a wheel are equivalent to time distances. Thus the symbol system in a watch—the watch's code alphabet—consists in the number of cogs on a wheel corresponding to so much time. Of course, this is a very rudimentary sort of code, for it does not allow for changes of sequential order to alter meaning. Distances alone count. But it bears the stamp of a rudimentary code in that certain cog distances in millimeters stand for certain distances in time. To construct such a rudimentary code as a watch is merely a matter of metallurgy and applied mathematics.

These operations basically represent a process of removing random arrangements of matter and replacing them by ordered sequences. In a specialized sense the whole watch construction process consists of an operation involving the reduction of entropy status and incurs "man-hours" and intellectual energy expenditure. The "derandomization of matter," even in the interest of the production of a primitive code, always costs energy. The latter may consist of measurable calories and ergs or the more imponderable but still measurable intellectual effort involved in mathematics. The physical work involved in this "derandomization" of matter, together with the intellectual work necessary, is relatable to energy, so that it is clear that energy or work and "order" (arising from "derandomization" processes) that is, sequences, can be related. The information involved in setting up sequences and codes can be directly related to entropy and work, as a later chapter will show.

It is possible to take a further step of logic in saying that, in general, matter tends to decay as far as order is concerned, if it is left to itself. However, if certain forms of energy are taken up by matter, then "derandomization" of matter can occur. Thus the "derandomization," or the sorting out of matter, is related to the expenditure of both physical energy (which we measure in calories and ergs) and the kind which is more imponderable but just as real—intellectual work.

We conclude that order in our material universe always tends to decrease until total randomization of matter reigns. Order can, however, be increased locally, provided we can apply work to it locally to derandomize it. The microsphere and coacervate research we have been discussing in the previous chapter represents an attempt by materialistic scientists to show that if random matter is irradiated with energy, such as that derived from the sun, it will finance the derandomization of biomonomers up to the morphogenicity of coacervates and microspheres which are alleged to be, in fact, protocells.

For the sake of clarity we must repeat that the kind of energy required to form biomonomers is not critical. Any energy "knock" is likely to land the elements of which biomonomers consist into the "low-lying entropy holes" of biomonomers because of the inherent order residing on them. But the ordering of biomonomers up to macromolecules of the coded sequences found in living material is an entirely different matter.

SEA WAVES AND COLUMNS OF WATER: AN ILLUSTRATION

For example, the entropy reduction required for amino acid synthesis (biomonomer synthesis) and that required for the sequential ordering of viable macromolecules is different because there is less free energetic choice in biomonomer formation than in specific macromolecular formation. In the latter there may be many thousands of choices of ways in which the reaction may go without any significant energy or work differences existing between the choices. This difference in energy relationships may be best expressed by an illustration.

The energy relationships required to form simple, ordinary waves in the calm sea and those that would be required to form and keep in position a thin spiral column of water of one foot in diameter from top to bottom and one thousand yards high are different in nature. Ordinary sea waves are easily formed and maintained by random energetic wind and tide action. But thin, tall, spiral columns of water of the above dimensions would be an altogether different proposition from the point of view of expended energy. For, in such a case, wind, tide and sea water viscosity would be insufficient to form and maintain such an exact spiral column of water. Let us add one more property to the column of water to make matters more comparable with those actually obtaining in life. At intervals on the spiral column of water, perhaps every fifteen inches, a piece of seaweed of a specified kind must project exactly three inches from the column and represent a code used in navigation by mariners! What forces would be required to keep such a specific system of structure and code sequence in being? They are comparable to the energy requirements necessary for the formation and maintenance of the DNA system.

Amino acids and other biomonomers, the smaller polypeptides together with the simpler proteins, are relatively easy to conceive of from an energetic point of view, just as are waves in a moderately choppy sea. But larger, sequenced, coded macromolecules are just as different a synthetic proposition as tall, thin, spiral columns of water, coded for mariners by seaweed markers, would be, compared to ordinary surf waves.

The grand problem of protobiology resolves itself, therefore, into one of accounting for the original formation of a highly complex derandomization of matter to produce the codes and sequences of life. It is clear that pure random processes cannot derandomize without some mechanism for doing so. And this mechanism must not collide with the known laws of thermodynamics. Random matter, left to itself, does not habitually or spontaneously derandomize itself —not even if irradiated with sunlight or X rays. We need to be able to account for the large coded molecules on which life rides and which today are synthesized only by living material —but without the help of biological life. For living material and enzymes possess the faculty of being able to supply energy necessary to derandomize matter in a way that other material does not. Living matter and some of its derivatives are able to construct the equivalents of a "thousand yards high, spiral columns of water peppered with coded seaweed" with impunity, which matter, without the help of life, does not succeed in producing.

To get around this difficulty some scientists have proposed that life began by riding on simple molecules.[1] But how it could do this and still obtain the metabolic energy necessary for life is difficult to envisage. Others, such as Richard S. Young, suggest that the beginning of life occurred when one molecule of nucleic acid became synthesized: "A molecule of nucleic acid or nucleoprotein can be equated with the 'beginning of life.' "[2] How it arose is anyone's guess, for it involves energy considerations which do not obtain "raw" in nature so as to produce nucleic acid molecules spontaneously.

Young rejects Oparin's attempt to bridge the huge gap existing between spontaneously arising organic biomonomers and living, metabolizing sequenced macromolecules by postulating the intermediate step of coacervates and microspheres. Young's basis for this rejection is that coacervates are structurally quite unstable and also of much too low a molecular weight. This is why Young thinks we shall have to short-circuit the whole problem as insoluble and simply define life as having begun when the first self-replicating nucleic acid molecule arose. One is almost tempted to remind the scientific materialists that at this point they are appealing to the supernatural and miraculous. For the spontaneous formation of such coded macromolecules is inconceivable in terms of random, natural processes—and therefore miraculous, if viewed as spontaneous.

ARCHEBIOPOESIS AND DNA

Carl Sagan believes with many other scientists that in primitive times the chances for production of DNA polymerase or polynucleotide phosphorylase (the enzymes responsible for DNA synthesis in the living cell) must have been very unlikely indeed. He points out:

> We need enzymes to make polynucleotides, and polynucleotides to make enzymes. As a possible way out of this quandary, I would like to suggest that we can trade geological time for DNA polymerase or polynucleotide phosphorylase. This problem is solved, if, in a short time compared with the age of the earth, but long compared with the lifetime of an average contemporary organism, the spontaneous polymerisation of the nucleotide triphosphatases can occur in the primitive oceans.

In actual fact, of course, we have no evidence at all that

this can occur, so the problem is still left unsolved.

The question of the protobiology of DNA and the enzymes concerned with its synthesis brings us to the general problem of the genetic code and its origin.

THE GENETIC CODE

One of the great results of modern molecular biology has been the development of the concept of the genetic code as the basis of heredity and metabolism.

As viewed at present, the code consists of three consecutive letters in an alphabet of four types. Corresponding to every triplet of the possible sixty-four there is some amino acid. Although the elucidation of the genetic code represents an enormous advance in knowledge there is still a great deal of ground to be broken before knowledge of the code's mechanism is complete.

M. Eden points out that molecular biology may well have given science the *alphabet* of the genetic code but that it is a long step to understanding the *language*.[4] To have learned the Greek alphabet is by no means the same thing as to have learned the Greek language. It is commonly assumed in Neo-Darwinian and other circles that at archebiopoesis a primitive genetic alphabet arose, followed by a primitive genetic code. The mechanism imputed to this synthesis is either that of random reactions over huge time periods or, more recently, that the code was inherent on the properties of the atoms constituting matter. Once the code had been set up, random mutations occurred in it, which sorted themselves out by natural selection, which was the means of their preservation as well as their improvement.

Eden elaborates on the difficulties facing such a scheme of things:

> No currently existing formal language can tolerate random changes in the symbol sequences which express its sentences. Meaning is invariably destroyed. Any changes must be syntactically lawful ones.[5]

What Eden means is that one can scarcely expect to improve a sentence or even to construct a novel from it by the process of taking the simple sentence, changing a few of its letters, and then adding random letters to it.

These fundamental difficulties of imagining the random and spontaneous development of a language from a randomly formed and sorted alphabet and random sentences are described still further by Eden:

> What I am claiming is simply that without some constraint on the motion of random variation in either the properties of the organism or the sequence of the DNA there is no particular reason to expect that we could have gotten any kind of viable form other than nonsense. It is the *character of the constraint* that makes things possible, not the variation. That is the point I am trying to make.[6]

Eden goes on to show that random processes are destructive of the syntactical order inherent in any code system and lead inevitably to nonsense rather than to the evolution of code order. For this purpose he uses recent cybernetic experience which has been gained by simulating biological evolutionary theory on powerful computers.

> Every attempt to provide for computer learning by random variation in some aspect of the program and by selection has been spectacularly unsuccessful, even though the number of variants a computer can try can easily run into billions. Of course, the simple explanation may be that the computer programmers weren't smart enough to set up the problem right. It seems to me that an adequate theory of adaptive evolution would supply the computer programmer with the correct set of ground rules, and perhaps it will some day.[7]

The point is, of course, that, as things stand today, random and adaptive evolutionary theories have not yet supplied the programming ground rules for extracting order spontaneously from random processes or for constraining such processes.

Surely this fact can only mean that some fundamental gaps still exist in current Neo-Darwinian theories which allegedly account for evolution as a result of random processes followed by competitive selection.

If the origin of real languages offers any parallel to the origin of the genetic language (or code), the principles on which Neo-Darwinians attempt to explain the genetic code origin certainly do not seem to apply. Indeed, the very opposite to the Neo-Darwinian position would seem to exist in respect to the postulated origin of languages. Some language experts believe that the more useful and sophisticated a language becomes, the simpler its internal grammar grows. Languages such as Eskimo and Hebrew were immensely complex in their early structure, but decayed in complexity, as time progressed, to rather simpler forms.

This brings to our minds the probable validity in linguistics of the second law of thermodynamics! The same is true of other languages such as English and Russian, as well as German. The old idea, to which Darwin himself adhered, that languages develop and evolve upward in grammar and complexity from the primitive howl or snort of a disgruntled or satisfied animal has limited support today. If the origin of languages offers any light at all on the origin of the genetic language (which, of course, it may not), might it not show that the genetic code, like the language code, was initially even more complex than at later periods? Both are forms of information codes.

If we are, in fact, dealing with a decaying rather than with a developing genetic code which was once even more complex than it is now, the mathematical problems of its origin would be even more difficult than they now are. If the complexity of the genetic code today is difficult to account for on the basis of random processes, how much more difficult would it be to account for if at its origin it were even more complex in code structure?

This and other similar reasons have caused a general swing away from the idea of purely random reactions as accounting for archebiopoesis. Many are busy postulating forms of restraint on random processes. But, the moment we introduce constraint on random processes, these processes can no longer truly be called "random." Many such scientists, among them Teilhard de Chardin, believe that built-in constraints are present in matter which allow no real random processes to occur at all. These ideas are crystallized in the theory of biochemical predestination, which we have already glanced at.

Often forgotten in discussions of this subject is the following: Certain amino acids and sulphur compounds will, under favorable conditions, combine together to produce the highly sequenced, biologically coded molecule known as insulin. It would, however, be incorrect to maintain that insulin synthesis from its constituent building blocks was *solely* a result of the inherent chemical properties of those building blocks plus kilogram calories. In one sense it is true, of course, that no synthesis can take place without the inherent chemical properties of the constituent atoms and radicals. But it is equally true that no synthesis can take place without two factors besides inherent chemistry: an adequate energy supply in kilogram calories, together with either a suitable specific catalyst or a scientist to manipulate conditions and induce the reaction to go in the desired direction. The association of all three factors leads to the correct synthesis. One without the others may lead to no synthesis or to nonspecificity.

Constraint of some sort, either by a presiding scientist or by a specific catalyst, is a *conditio sine qua non* for reactions where many pathways are possible. Without constraint, nonspecificity is surely arrived at, for the inherent properties of the constituent atoms and radicals will lead to combination but not to specific sequenced combination.

THE NATURE OF CONSTRAINTS IN MACROMOLECULAR SYNTHESIS

In macromolecular synthesis where many reaction pathways are possible there are obviously many choices to be made if a specific synthetic molecule is to be arrived at. We have already mentioned this problem. Many have attempted to circumvent the theoretical impasse arising from the Darwinian concept of randomness as a controlling factor in such reactions. Lerner, for example, suggested that there are various "automatic" restrictions, inherent in the constituent elements, which exercise restraint on reaction pathways.[8] This is an idea similar to that put forward by Kenyon, which we have already discussed. Following this line of thought, Crosby has pointed out that heating of random mixtures of amino acids under certain conditions produces polymers of remarkably limited heterogeneity. He therefore deduces that "random" polymer formation is, in fact, intrinsically limited or constrained in favor of certain specific polymers.[9] This means that the inherent properties of the amino acid constituents totally guide or constrain the polymerization pathway. Which again means that randomness, as imagined by the earlier Darwinians, is really not very random.

Most organic chemists who have worked on the synthesis of diastereoisomers know of phenomena of this kind. One diastereoisomer is usually produced at the expense of other possible random isomers. There are usually sound steric reasons for this type of constraint on randomness. But equally sound reasons are to be found for doubting whether this well-known principle of diastereoisomerism could be called upon to account for the huge constraints which must have been operative in the biosynthesis of primeval living proteins or nucleic acids.

The problem is, once again, not merely of specificity in polymers or diastereoisomers. It is that of the formation of a sequenced *code* in living genes and proteins, not merely that of a specific chemical isomer. A whole molecule in synthesis of the type we are discussing is a code conveying information. That is, there is the matter of a code specificity superimposed on the matter of a macromolecular stereospecificity. Compared with the imposition of a code sequence on a molecule, the imposition of even optical isomerism on a molecule is relatively simple. The explanation of the *origin* of a code is far more difficult.

When some scientists claim that a number of proteins are really close to purely random molecules, one suspects a certain amount of hedging in order to circumvent the real nature of the problem, which is that of specificity, or nonrandomness.[10] However, it is quite certain that the coded sequences of the nucleic acids and the resultant proteins are *not* random in nature. And most viable proteins are anything but random in structure, so that the problem of constraint cannot be swept under the carpet by maintaining that some viable proteins are near to random structure. Even if one viable protein were of random structure, this randomness would not explain the other viable nonrandom proteins.

One can only assume, therefore, that considerable and effective constraints were active during the synthesis of specific viable molecules, and that these constraints were greatly stepped up during the production of coded sequences in such molecules.

CONSTRAINT AND PROBABILITY

In some circles it has been common practice to try to circumvent this whole problem of the origin of constraint in the synthesis of specificity and code sequences by allowing randomness and long time periods to explain everything. If one allows enough time, the reasoning goes, anything will happen, including constraints in reactions to produce sequences and codes. This argument has been a favorite one with the older generation of Darwinians and one with which I have dealt in detail elsewhere.[11]

Peter T. Mora, writing on the subject, "the Folly of Probability," deals with the attempted explanations of the mechanisms governing the probable evolution of living matter from nonliving substrates. He treats in some detail this tendency to explain away everything, even the problem of constraints in synthesis, and maintains:

A further practice which I should like to discuss is what I call the infinite escape clauses. I believe we developed this practice to avoid facing the conclusion that *the probability of a self-reproducing state is zero.* This is what we must conclude from classical quantum mechanical principles, as Wigner demonstrated in 1961. [12] These escape clauses postulate an almost infinite amount of time and an almost infinite amount of material [monomers], so that even the most unlikely event could have happened. *This is to invoke probability and statistical considerations when such considerations are meaningless. When for practical purposes the condition of infinite time and matter has to be invoked, the concept of probability is annulled. By such logic we can prove anything, such as that no matter how complex, everything will repeat itself, exactly and innumerably.* [13]

The above citation from Mora admirably expresses our view concerning the basis of infinite-time hypotheses in random processes. For the practice of invoking infinite time to explain orderly syntheses showing constraint adds up to this maxim: "If in doubt about a mechanism or its probability, add a few million years to the equation to be solved." Adding a few million years when in doubt has worked like a charm since Darwin's time, for it has seemed to cure even the most chronic thermodynamic and mechanistic ills.

Continuing this line of thought, Mora adds:

Another futile argument is that the conditions [under which abiogenesis took place] may have changed drastically and many other types of life may have started which are extinct now. This argument removes speculation from the field of physico-chemical knowledge by not allowing us to extrapolate backward. *My point is that we have no way to prove or disprove such statements, and this efficiently removes them from the domain of science.* [14]

THE NATURE OF SPECIFICITY AND BIOLOGICAL CODING

Let us now take stock of the present theoretical situation

in accounting for the high specificity plus the complex coding found in matter on which life rides.

Darwinians and Neo-Darwinians have long maintained that randomness, plus long time spans, plus natural selection would, in combination, do the synthetic trick and deliver specific codes and molecules. However, recent progress in cybernetics has shown by simulation experiments that order sequences, specificity and coding cannot be extracted from randomness on the basis of the Darwinian postulates.

More recently, therefore, other scientists have suggested that there is no such thing as true randomness in nature. For, according to these views, order is hidden in the atoms and radicals on which life rides. This inherent order will work itself out inevitably and inexorably wherever and whenever the conditions are favorable. Darwin attributed everything to chance, whereas Kenyon denies all real chance in accounting for abiogenesis.

Teilhard de Chardin also believed this latter view and endeavored to base his harmony of Christianity with evolutionary theory on the same hypothesis. Scientists such as Kenyon and Steinman believe the same way, but they use the theory to bolster up their particular brand of scientific materialism, for they emphasize that, if their theory is true, then no supernatural interference was necessary to account for the appearance of life on the earth. They forget the question of *the origin of their postulated inherent order* on atoms and radicals. This order is alleged to be responsible for spontaneous ordered upward evolution. Thus they have really only succeeded in pushing the basic problem—that of order arising from chaos spontaneously—one step further back.

Whichever way we look at the problem of the appearance of order from randomness—whether we use the Teilhard brand of theory or that of biochemical predestination—if we assume that oder arose spontaneously from chaos, we shall collide sooner or later with the laws of thermodynamics. It does not matter whether we hold that *atoms and radicals* ordered themselves spontaneously or whether the *order or algorithms* inherent in the atoms arose spontaneously, the end result is thermodynamically identical. If we use solar or radioactive energy to finance order, *we have to have a metabolic motor* of some sort to mediate it. Yet, how can we assume that the order of a motor—an exceedingly complex matter—arose spontaneously?

To propose that even protein specificity arose on the basis of randomness—true randomness—is to misunderstand the laws of thermodynamics. But to propose that coding, as opposed to mere molecular specificity, arose on the same basis, is even more implausible. Codes are obviously associated with intelligent communication somewhere along the line. We assume, then, that the origin of meaningful codes— even the genetic code—is associated with an origin in meaningful thought. In fact, the patterns of nonliving matter lead some physicists (Sir James Jeans is an example) to postulate an origin in thought, and the patterns and codes of living matter lead to a similar postulate, both for the same reason.

1. M. E. Jones, L. Spector and F. Lippmann, *J. Amer. Chem. Soc.*, 62 (1955): 819.

2. Richard S. Young, article in S. W. Fox, ed. *The Origins of Prebiological Systems*, pp. 347-48.

3. Carl Sagan, article in *The Origins . . .* , p. 215.

4. M. Eden, article in P. S. Moorhead and M. M. Kaplan, eds., *Mathematical Challenges to the Neo-Darwinian Interpretation of Evolution*, p. 11.

5. Ibid., p. 14.

6. Ibid.

7. Ibid.

8. Michael Lerner, article in *Mathematical Challenges . . .* , p. 16.

9. J. L. Crosby, article in *Mathematical Challenges . . .* , p. 17.

10. George Gamov, Alexander Rich and Martynas Yčas, "The Problem of Information Transfer from Nucleic Acids to Proteins," in *Advances in Biological and Medical Physics*, 4:23, as cited in *Mathematical Challenges . . .* , p. 17 (cf. p. 19).

11. A. E. Wilder Smith, *Man's Origin, Man's Destiny*, pp. 52-109.

12. E. P. Wigner, *The Logic of Personal Knowledge*.

13. Peter T. Mora in *The Origins . . .* , p. 45.

14. Ibid., p. 46.

6.

biochemical predestination: further implications

In recent years, as we have already noticed, there has been a certain shift of opinion among scientific materialists insofar as the problem of the origin of life and the mechanism of chemical evolution is concerned.

The general consensus of opinion used to be—and in many quarters still is—that neobiogenesis is best explained as a highly improbable event or accident occurring only rarely, probably only once, in past history. This highly improbable accident was so very improbable that billions of years were required to achieve it.

The same type of thinking has not only governed the question of neobiogenesis (the development of living material from nonliving matter), but it has also governed the approach of many scientific materialists toward the whole question of biological evolution *after* neobiogenesis had taken place. Biological evolution is thought to have involved millions of years for its gradual development by the trial and error techniques, for it also depends on unlikely phenomena or accidents which require plenty of time.

In recent years there has been, as already remarked, a certain shift away from this "accidental" position. Perhaps one reason for this change has been that the view is not susceptible to experiment, except that of computer simulation. Thus the whole idea of accidents over billions of years really lies outside the realm of traditional scientific experiment.

The scientific materialists have long been considering how they can satisfactorily replace this accident theory by something better but still materialistic. Kenyon's theory of biochemical predestination represents one attempt at a solution of this problem.

As already noted, the theory of biochemical predestination teaches that the steps leading up to life and life's evolution afterward were really decided upon with the appearance of matter itself. When matter arose it allegedly became endowed with the total code, or algorithm, leading inevitably and inexorably up to life and to man. Accordingly, Kenyon teaches that it will some day be possible to

> predict the overall structure of a given polypeptide on the basis of its primary sequence alone. In some sense, we should eventually be able to predict the overall course of evolution, both prebiogenetic and Darwinian, on the basis of a known assemblage of starting compounds with particular properties and a given set of environmental circumstances, as the theory of Biochemical Predestination suggests. [1]

Continuing the same line of thought, Kenyon proceeds:

> What the theory of Biochemical Predestination would tell us, however, is that the choices that would be made, i.e., the limits beyond which evolutionary processes could not stray, would be determined largely by properties inherent

in the evolving bodies as preset by the materials from which
the materials were fabricated.[2]

The consequences of these explicit statements are manifold. Primary among them is the implication that each elementary building block of life received at its formation a
complete code, or algorithm, of *all* later evolutionary development. Elementary particles, on this basis, are constructed
something like a sperm or ovum. They contain the "genes" or
programming for all later life of which they will become a
part. Their complexity must be, on this basis, enormous, for
the complexity of a biomonomer is permanent. It does not
decay in death, as does a gene. The biomonomer's order is
perfect and permanent for all generations, so that its coding
must be a coding for life's patterns from the beginning to the
end of life.

In accordance with this belief, Kenyon and his colleagues
believe that each building block of hemoglobin, for example,
hides in its inherent properties all the directions needed to
build the total molecule from its biomonomers. This conception makes "simple" matter, "simple" building blocks,
veritable mines of information consisting of orders and codes
of the most complex kind.

Kenyon believes that his conclusion is justified on the basis
that when certain biomonomers combine to give the biodimers, they often do so in preferred ways determined by
their inherent properties. "Nearest neighbor interaction" is a
major force determining sequence generation in monomer to
dimer reactions. Kenyon believes that this property will decide not only the sequence of dimers, but also those of all the
higher polymers which can be formed by further polymerization. Consequently, the properties of and the synthetic
route to the most complex biopolymers are decided upon
exclusively by the inherent properties resident on the simple
chemical building blocks of which the higher biopolymers are
constructed. A lesser value is thereby set upon the exogenous
factors surrounding the reacting monomers. It is the inherent
factors which are decisive.

So that there can be no misunderstanding about this position, Kenyon reiterates it time and time again:

> B: You recall we discussed evidence showing that if you arrange the probabilities of formation of the different dimers of a number of particular amino acids from the most probable dimer down to the least probable and then construct a similar scale based on analysis of *contemporary protein sequences* . . . you find that the two sets of probability data show surprisingly similar trends.
>
> A: That's right: so, in summary, we can state first, that we can account for the appearance of biomonomers under possible primitive conditions.
>
> B: Yes.
>
> A: In addition, we see that the polymerization of these units also could have occurred quite readily under primitive conditions.
>
> B: Yes, I agree with that.
>
> A: And not only do we observe the production of biopolymers, but these biopolymers apparently contain certain specific sequences which have been determined by characteristics inherent in the coming together of the units.
>
> B: That's right: but isn't it true that so far we've only studied the formation of dimers, so we don't know really how far this sequence specificity extends?
>
> A: Yes, but the chemical nature of the *peptide bond* at the dimer level is essentially the same as that found at the polymer level. Therefore, I suspect that those phenomena which we observe at the dimer level play a major role at the polymer level as well.
>
> B: You're saying, then, that a major force which determines sequence generation is the *nearest neighbor interaction*.[3]

Kenyon here maintains that the nature of the peptide bond decides the sequences. A lesser value is put on exogenous forces in specific sequence formation. Greatest weight is placed on internal molecular and atomic factors rather than on external ones. Under the correct conditions, the building blocks allegedly possess sufficient inherent directive forces to guide them right up to the most complex macromolecules of life without their being dependent on exogenous guidance. That is, given the random building blocks plus random free energy, the biomonomers can allegedly direct the rest of the chemical operations up to life on their own. They contain sufficient chemical and other information to undertake autonomously the total synthesis.

SOME CONSEQUENCES OF BIOCHEMICAL PREDESTINATION

Kenyon's theory would lead us to believe, in essence, that life is by no means an accident but that it is based on a secret hidden in nonliving matter. Accordingly, life would be expected to arise anywhere and everywhere where conditions are suitable. In fact, life is the very opposite of an accidental occurrence (the Darwinian position), for it is blueprinted in every biomonomer on which it rides.

Life would thus be expected to arise inexorably all over the universe wherever matter exists. If matter on other planets or universes is the same as our matter it must be blueprinted for life just as our matter is. A corollary of this belief is that if life arises extraterrestrially on matter on the distant planets, its form everywhere will be comparable to life's form as we know it here on the earth. It is blueprinted on matter there in just the same way as it is here.

Another consequence of the theory is that matter is even more vastly complex than we suspected. It must be a storehouse of information vastly exceeding in complexity that of the gene, for it is an algorithm of life, besides being everything else we know it to be. This consequence comes very close to flying in the face of the second law of thermodynamics. For this law describes matter as being loaded with a tendency toward disorder unless rather special precautions, such as energy supplies of a particular kind, are taken. In contrast, Kenyon believes that, left to itself under favorable conditions, matter is loaded with a tendency to order itself up to life when supplied with spontaneous random energy.

Kenyon and his friends probably see this looming thermodynamic cliff in the mists of their speculations and try to circumnavigate it by invoking the work of Onsager, Prigogine and others who state that, in closed systems, maximum entropy or disorder is reached, but that in open thermodynamic systems, in which energy exchanges are possible, there is a tendency to reach a state in which *minimum changes of entropy* occur at any particular level.[4]

A question is perhaps the best answer to this kind of proposition. Why, then, have such *huge reductions* in entropy taken place in an open system such as this earth offers, in that life *has* been formed? For Kenyon, basing his work on that of Onsager, has maintained just the opposite—that *minimum* changes of entropy will occur. The supposed phenomenon of spontaneous neobiogenesis cannot possibly represent a *minimal change of entropy*. If this is the case, then Kenyon has no right to appeal to Onsager's work in his attempt to slip around the entropy problem and the second law. For very large reductions or changes in entropy must have occurred when life appeared.

A further consequence of Kenyon's theory is brought out if we ask ourselves the following question: What was *the origin of the huge source of information*, allegedly stored on elementary particles to enable them to develop upward to life? Whether these storage sites of life's information code are thought of as atoms or as biomonomers is immaterial for our present purposes. If these elementary building blocks of life are life's algorithms, as Kenyon suggests, *when and how were they programmed*? For programming of this exquisitely complex and miniaturized type can never be assumed, by anyone who knows even the rudiments of information theory, to have arisen as a result of random spontaneous forces.

Still another consequence of Kenyon's speculations is brought out when we ask why scientists have experienced such difficulties in observing the proposed programming on the building blocks of life. Let us face up to it: in spite of all

Kenyon's evidence that morphogenicity resides on amino acids and other biomonomers, no one has ever observed even a simple viable molecule such as insulin arising spontaneously in reasonable yields under random conditions in mixtures of its monomers. If Kenyon is correct, this ought to be an everyday occurrence.

On the contrary, it has taken an inordinate amount of exogenous "information input" in the form of well-planned flow sheets and chemical skill in order to arrive at a successful synthesis of even a comparatively simple substance like insulin. The same considerations apply to other simple proteins and hormones. We see little of this "inherent programming" of insulin or other building blocks straining at the leash to arrange themselves autonomously into the stereospecificity and sequences of the complete, physiologically active insulin molecule. To arrive at such a molecule the information contained in the form of chemical bonds on the elementary particles must be supplemented by huge amounts of additional information which is supplied by the presiding scientist or by the catalyst active in this particular reaction.

Similarly, the inherent constraints and chemical properties resident in the basic building blocks of hemoglobin, plasma proteins, etc., have never been shown to push them unerringly upward to the sequences they assume in the molecules of living matter. There is no acceptable evidence that enough of this alleged "inherent information" resides on the basic building blocks of these biological molecules to achieve the desired goal *unaided by exogenous sources of information.*

To guard against misunderstanding, we must reemphasize that steric hindrance and other chemical directive constraints are certainly present which, in preventing one isomer from being formed, may favor the formation of an alternative isomer. But this phenomenon usually takes place most effectively in lower polymers, such as dimers, where relative differences between structures and geometry are larger, percentagewise, than in higher polymers. Higher up the scale, and in the case of optical isomerism, more is needed than this class of constraint to decide and determine which isomer, or optical isomer, is to be formed. Any scientist familiar with the processes of optical resolution in the laboratory will understand what is involved in constraints of the type we are referring to.

In spite of all the technical and theoretical difficulties which confront us in accounting for the constraints of life, *the metabolism of life* shows not the slightest difficulty or hesitancy in synthesizing even optical isomers under the mildest conditions. *Where did it obtain its precise directive information to achieve these marvels of chemical precision with so little fuss?*

The appearance in certain dimers of spontaneous sequences, on which Kenyon lays so much weight, can very easily be accounted for by such phenomena as steric hindrance. For the relative differences in properties between one dimer and another, as already mentioned, are fairly large. But in the higher polymers the percentage differences in properties are likely to be much less, with the result that the constraints necessary to effect their distinction in synthesis are more difficult to arrive at.

These relationships may be best made clear by the following illustration.

MAZE-RUNNING AND MICE

The synthesis of a plasma protein from its building blocks may be compared to running a maze using mice as experimental tools. The entrance to the maze may be compared to the commencement of the protein synthesis. The maze exit— for our purpose there is only one—simulates the arrival at the final synthetic product, the plasma protein. Every turn in the maze represents a synthetic chemical reaction leading either up to the desired plasma protein or to some dead-end undesired product. To successfully run the maze, the mouse must make the correct left or right turn at each fork in the path, that is, at each synthetic reaction.

At the entry to this synthetic maze the starting building

block or blocks must turn either "right" or "left." This means that there is a choice—either to undergo or not to undergo the correct reaction leading to the desired exit or end product. If the wrong turn is taken at this stage, no subsequent decisions will ever lead to the correct end product or exit. But if the initial decision, be it right or left, is correctly made, then there is a chance of arriving at the desired exit, though a wrong decision at any point along the way will prevent arrival at the desired end point.

The decision-making in this type of maze-running may be based on simple chemical laws, either of steric hindrance, nearest-neighbor relationships or others. But it would be a remarkable maze, and indeed a remarkable synthesis, in which all decisions were made successfully on the basis of one inherent property. Kenyon's propositions seem to fall into this category. If this were the basis of running a maze (all "lefts" or all "rights"), then a maze could scarcely be called a maze, for all right turns—or all left turns—would eventually lead to the desired exit. If the first turn on entering the maze was made on the basis of the properties of a peptide bond and was a "left," then all subsequent turns would be "lefts" too and the maze would be no maze. It is as though all mice were put into the maze having a congenital defect causing them, whenever in doubt, to turn left.

The plain fact is, that the synthetic mazes of nature are real mazes and congenitally defective left-turn mice—or biomonomers which always react one way at the expense of another—are a fiction of the mind. Biomonomers do not automatically run the synthetic maze up to viable proteins for the simple reason that they do not inherently "know" the way through the maze. For the way is far more complex than simply turning left when in doubt. This is not the technique that scientists have been able to use in synthesizing life's products.

How does a scientist help biomonomers of insulin, for example, to run the insulin maze? He "feeds" information to them and thus "nudges" them the correct way. Without this exogenous feeding activity, "mice" will certainly go astray in the maze. How does the scientist feed this information into the synthetic maze? He isolates the various reaction stages and then loads the corners and turnings, half blocking one way and widening the other so as to coax his "mice," the biopolymers, in the way they should go. Or he uses a catalyst which favors one turn at the expense of another because of its stereochemical surface structure. Some catalysts seem to contain in their structures a complete code of information which is used by the biomonomers to run the particular turn at which they are inserted into the maze system.

We must emphasize again that no real maze is ever run on the basis (as Kenyon appears to maintain) that if the mouse always takes the same turn from beginning to end it will arrive at the correct exit. For, if a "synthetic" maze could be run on the basis of "always take a left" to reach the desired exit, then any mixture of the correct biomonomers which undergoes the correct first reaction or turn should automatically run the rest of the maze successfully on the same basis. In real chemical syntheses, things do not work out this way. The great difficulty in real chemical syntheses or mazes lies in the fact that there is a variety of turns possible at each fork in the route. The problem is to get the *right information* to the biopolymers at the right place at the right time.

By the time our synthetic process has run through the entire maze leading up to insulin or a plasma protein, for example, perhaps thousands of decisions, each vital if the correct goal is to be reached, will have been made correctly.

If chance has been the master architect in running the synthetic maze then the likelihood of successfully running a multistage maze becomes smaller with every stage involved. For the awkward fact must be faced that in the synthesis of large molecules, chemically speaking, it is often just as easy to take a "right" as it is to take a "left." So there will be cases where the maze-running, if dependent on chance, would run at the rate of 50 percent "wrong" at each turn. The result would be that the chances of arriving at the exit would be vanishingly small by the time very few decisions had been made.

We can now sum up Kenyon's proposals in terms of the maze-running illustration. He and his colleagues are, in effect, saying that the biological synthetic maze leading through chemical evolution up to abiogenesis is predestined to be run correctly and inevitably simply because the "mice" are "genetically" predisposed to navigate it. No exogenous scientific skill or information beyond that which is inherent in the mice is needed to help them through the maze. If we extrapolate this thought a little we shall see that it is *a denial of the necessity of all technique and technological skill in the synthesis of life in the test tube.* Accordingly, if biochemical predestination is correct, scientists are wasting their time contriving chemical reactions in their efforts to extract life's order from reaction systems. The correct way through the maze is, allegedly, coded in the biomonomers. Thus, our efforts should instead be directed toward extracting this alleged endogenous code in them, for the code is bound to be correct, if Kenyon is right, and must lead us by the surest route to our desired exit, or viable end product.

INHERENT PROPERTIES MANDATORY

In spite of this it will still be obvious that no life riding on matter could exist unless life's building blocks contained the basic inherent properties of specific chemical combination. Nor could they combine with one another unless free energy were supplied to make combination possible. To use our illustration of the maze-running mice, no mice could run the maze unless they possessed the facility of locomotion and unless they obtained the energy for movement by metabolizing food. In biomonomers inherent ability to combine (locomotion) and the energy from metabolism to do it (energy availability) are both mandatory. But these two factors are not all-sufficient. A third one, about which we have been speaking, that of direction and ability to make a choice, is just as necessary if we are to arrive at the exit. Kenyon claims that this directive ability is inbuilt in biomonomers. We claim that it is mostly supplied exogenously to biomonomers by feeding in chemical skills or applying specific catalysts.

The older view, in terms of the maze-running analogy, taught that the synthetic maze up to life and beyond was run "systematically" by chance. Today this is manifestly impossible and implausible. Therefore there is a switch in view which maintains that chance is so implausible that the ability must lie in the genetic makeup of the mice (that is, the biomonomers). The old view fails on the basis of sheer implausibility and conflict with information theory. The new view really founders on its being in conflict with the basic properties of matter, which do not tend to spontaneous order, but to disorder.

The older view (that life is an unlikely accident) has been demonstrated to be not only implausible but experimentally unsound in simulation experiments on large computers. This we have already mentioned. Since scientists in general seem to realize the basic weakness of Kenyon's views, there has been a great unwillingness to exchange the old views for the new—and understandably so. But what has science to offer which is better on a purely material basis?

BOWING TO THE EVIDENCE

The unwillingness to abandon the foundering ship of Darwinian chance hypothesis came out quite surprisingly in the symposium mentioned in chapter 1. The following citation shows the fundamental unwillingness to submit to the only sound experimental evidence available on the subject:

"Dr. Schützenberger: I want to know how I can build on computers, programs which. . . . "

The chairman, Dr. Waddington: "We are not interested in your computers!"[5]

Try as he might to show the importance of simulated evidence where actual experimental evidence is not available and never can be, (involving, as it does, millions of years which must be simulated much as we simulate car and aircraft accidents or flights) Dr. Schützenberger was unable to get a fair hearing devoid of what may be termed heckling.

Today it is no longer true that the evidence is lacking to refute scientific materialism based on either the accident or the predestination hypotheses of life's origin. The evidence is available to thoroughly rout it. But he who attempts to do so will be scientifically, and effectively, "lynched" for his pains. What is less available than the evidence is the willingness to bow to clear evidence which makes nonsense of much that passes for science in the world of materialistic Neo-Darwinism.

THE ORIGIN OF CONSTRAINT

A matter of fundamental theoretical importance, which, as far as I can see, Kenyon and his colleagues never mention, is the precise origin of the coded restraint which they believe is resident on biomonomers.

In principle, of course, it is immaterial whether the coded restraint applied to direct the running of a maze is of endogenous nature, that is, resident on the biomonomers, or whether it is of exogenous origin. As long as the maze-running mice or biomonomers obtain their coded information, it does not matter whether its source is endogenous or exogenous.

But one matter in this area is of vast importance: Where did the exogenous or endogenous coding come from in the first place? Most scientific materialists seem to assume, if they give the matter thought at all, that the source of the coded information is, like every other aspect of their views, a product of randomness. Randomness is supposed to have gradually brought forth order. As we have already seen, such an explanation is no explanation for the reason that randomness (or "noise" in information theory) is the archenemy of coding systems.

Thus, to do as Kenyon does in dealing with these problems is merely to sweep them under the carpet. In effect, he is saying that the "Darwinian" *randomness* of nature is, on theoretical grounds, unable to be made responsible for the order of life. He therefore pushes the problem a stage further back and says that the *order* of life came from an order resident on biomonomers ("Biochemical Predestination"). But on what resources did the biomonomers draw to obtain their order if they had only nature's randomness at their disposal? *The point is that, if life's order could not arise from randomness, neither could a biomonomer's coding order arise spontaneously from randomness. If viable macromolucules cannot get their order spontaneously from chaos, how could biomonomers—or even atoms—obtain their order for the coding of life's syntheses spontaneously from the same source, namely, chaos?* This is rather like Admiral Nelson's attitude to his commander. The latter sent him a clear order to retreat, but the worthy Nelson put his telescope to his blind eye and truthfully said, afterward, that he had never seen the message.

Kenyon, and others with him, land in all these theoretical difficulties for one very simple reason. They are unwilling to admit the necessity of any outside organizing influence on matter as far as the appearance of life's codes and their maintenance are concerned. They know that chance will not do the trick, though many Neo-Darwinians still hang onto this sinking ship. *So, to avoid the necessity of the outside influence on matter, which would mean an immediate appeal to the supernatural, they propose appealing to internal, inherent material sources of the direction which they must have.*

What other possibilities are left to the scientific materialists? If no outside direction is allowed (this might involve the divine, and is therefore to be rejected at once), then they must look *inside*. Outside direction was in order as long as it was known as "chance." But now that chance has been thoroughly shot down, they must look elsewhere. The only place left to look is, of course, inside matter. But the fact is now rapidly emerging that it is as hopeless to examine the inherent properties of matter as it is to appeal to outside "chance" in explaining the order of life. For what was the source of the alleged "inside" order?

In all these considerations the important point to keep firmly in mind is that direction has been applied somehow or other to matter to produce life. If *nature as we know it* had been allowed to take over the problem of direction in our synthetic maze, it would certainly have supplied direction to it, "downward," to randomness. In our example of the synthetic maze, direction "upward" implies the direction toward the organization of life at the exit of the maze, but lesser organization and increased entropy are situated at the entry to the system. *This means that the direction which nature will spontaneously supply to our synthetic system will be "downward" to randomness and disorder.* For the exit is the area of the higher complexity of life over against the entrance, which is the area where the simple building blocks of life enter to be built up into the complexity of life.

In summary: nature, left to herself, will tend to produce only the starting materials, the biomonomers of life, the simple building blocks. And, nature, left to herself will produce death, not life; the basic decomposition or composition molecules of life rather than life's synthesis. That all nature does eventually travel in this direction—toward death rather than life—surely no one will dispute.

ANOTHER LOOK AT KENYON'S BIOMONOMER CONSTRAINT

Kenyon believes that a few inherent properties of biomonomers are sufficient to guide them up to full-blooded life. The properties resident on a simple peptide bond are, in Kenyon's eyes, the same as the properties resident on the same peptide bonds present in the largest protein macromolecules of life. That is, if a biomonomer X possesses a sequence, code or other properties which we will call a, b and c, then those same properties, a, b, and c, will persist on the same bond throughout the polymerizations leading up to life. In fact, a, b and c will supply the necessary direction for the total synthesis. Perhaps we can best look at this proposition with the help of another illustration.

Suppose we have on our hands an alphabet of some twenty-four letters with which to experiment. Our alphabet is of a rather special chemical kind: each letter is capable of combining with one or two other letters, providing that energy is supplied to activate the "valency" bonds of the letters. The order sequences in which the letter combinations can take place are largely determined by the random distribution of the letters. When one letter collides with another, combination is possible. Thus the concentration of the letters will play a role in deciding which sequences of letters turn up in the combinations. Finally, those letter sequences which correspond to code meanings (that is, words with a sense attached to them, like "put," "tub" or "mut") are assumed to be slightly more favored in their formation and will therefore occur more often.

The random combination of such alphabet letters will produce many code sequences with meanings, such as "a-n-d," "d-a-d," "t-a-b," "b-u-t" and "d-u-d." We may even get more complex sequences based on four-letter combinations such as "d-u-s-t," "s-t-u-b," "m-u-s-t" and "d-i-r-t." All these types of sequences will turn up among nonsensical ones like "m-r-t-h," "t-r-b-t" and "u-i-t-h," but as laid down above, the sequences with sense are preferred. Smaller as well as larger sequences can also appear, of course.

From this analogy it is clear that meaningful "codes" of a simple nature *can* turn up on the basis of chance. But it would be a brave man who would risk extrapolating this fact to include the production of a code consisting of sequences of the same twenty-four letters, known as Grey's *Elegy* or Shakespeare's *Hamlet*. The "a-n-d-s" and "b-u-t-s" are to be compared with the simple sequenced peptides cited by Kenyon as arising by random combination conditioned by nearest-neighbor relationships. The Grey's *Elegy* and Shakespeare's *Hamlet* sequences are analogous to proteins, enzymes, DNA and RNA molecules, and the scientific materialist is the brave man!

The letters in the alphabet, like biomonomers, possess inherent properties which give certain preferred sequences which may turn out simple codes. But biomonomers cannot give rise to complex macromolecules, just as alphabet letters cannot turn out, of themselves, a meaningful poem or a play. They do not possess the necessary overall purpose or direction.

What then does supply the direction up to life and its specifically sequenced macromolecules? It is our thesis that the answer to this question has been known for many years now, but up to the present it has not been consciously applied to the problem.

A SUGGESTED SOLUTION TO THE PROBLEM
OF CONSTRAINT AND DIRECTION IN SYNTHESIS.

It is our belief that a solution to the problem of the origin of constraint and direction in the running of life's synthetic maze has long been known but has been rejected to conform with the dogmas of scientific materialism. Let us briefly run through the evidence for our proposition.

Consider any reasonably complex multistage organic or biochemical synthetical flow sheet. (A flow sheet is a scheme setting out symbolically the various reaction stages and conditions under which the synthesis may be successfully carried out.) All details necessary from start to finish are indicated so that it may be carried out by anyone skilled in synthesis. As an example let us consider a hypothetical flow sheet for the synthesis of ascorbic acid (vitamin C), from its basic building blocks.

How does scientific technique today set about the problem of running this well-known synthetic maze? The principles are quite simple—at least when one knows the method from experience. At each stage of each reaction in the chain leading upward to the desired exit point the chemist controls physical and chemical reaction conditions in such a way as to erect "roadblocks" barring the entrance leading to undesired reaction products and to "widen" reaction pathways leading in the direction he desires. By this carefully organized technique, which is the result of a completely preconceived plan, he coaxes the reactants to make "left turns" and to avoid "right turns" in the synthetic maze.

While keeping the above in mind, it is important to stress the fact that the actual properties causing the reactants to combine—or not to combine—are inherently resident in them. In just the same way, the letters of our alphabet possessed the inherent property of combining by ones or twos or threes with one another. But the important point is this: The inherent properties of the chemicals reacting to form vitamin C need to be *encouraged in the right direction by "roadblocks" and "path-widening" activities* in the shape of manipulating reaction conditions according to the chemist's requirements. *In an analogous manner the letters of our alphabet possess the inherent property of combining with one another by ones or twos and can use this capacity independently and autonomously to form the "ands" and the "buts." However, they need a presiding writer to coax them into the more complex sequences of meaningful literature.*

Again, at the risk of repetition, it should be carefully noted that it would be of little use throwing all the necessary reactants for the vitamin C synthesis into a reaction vessel and stewing them up or cooling them in a haphazard way to supply energy requirements. The "bucket and soup" method yields minimal quantities of chemical products in synthetic exercises. *Every stage must be individually controlled so that the inherent properties resident on the synthetic building blocks are best exploited to reach the desired end.* The inherent properties of the building blocks must be used and are vitally necessary in any synthesis. But their capacity to direct themselves autonomously up to the complex macromolecules on which life rides is strictly limited. In order to attain this end, the inherent properties of the building blocks need an *"injection of information"* on the particular maze to be run. Either a presiding chemist or a suitable catalyst may be used for this purpose. The catalyst is merely a form of "canned" information and so serves the same ends as the "live" information furnished by the presiding scientist.

There are, of course, cases where the inherent properties of the building blocks are sufficient to direct them to simple specific end products. An obvious case is one we have already mentioned. When methane, steam and ammonia are reacted together in the presence of certain forms of free energy (electric sparks, electron beams, etc.), there is sufficient direction on their structures to direct them to the amino acid exit point. Many other simple—or less simple—exit points are attainable in other synthetic mazes by the same method. But the fact remains that, *as entropy becomes more and more reduced up to the maze exit point known as life itself, the clearer it becomes that the programming and direction necessary to reach this exit point are not inherent on the building blocks themselves.* Exogenous direction of these inherent properties is necessary to attain that exit point.

It is necessary, therefore, to spend a few moments looking at methods by which information can be injected into such syntheses.

"CANNED" INFORMATION

We have already glanced at the techniques by which a presiding scientist can coax his reactants along the maze pathways he desires. He changes concentrations, temperatures, pH values, irradiates with light or other sources of energy or adds a specific catalyst to the reacting system. This is done in research laboratories on a varied and, of course, purely individual basis. The scientist sits over—and often broods over—his synthesis!

But in modern syntheses carried out on a huge scale in factories we do not find scientists brooding over thousands of tons of reactants. The flow sheets have all been worked out on a small scale, then the information necessary for the small-scale run is translated to that required for large-scale operations and recorded on computers or other machines, so that it can be applied time and time again with little human interference. Machines and computers are programmed to alter conditions automatically at each reaction stage. In such cases exogenous direction and information are provided in a "canned" form. When the reaction was carried out the first few times on a research scale, the direct intervention by human intelligence was a requirement. Later, this direct intervention is no longer necessary, for the "intelligence" can be "canned" and successfully applied to guide the reactants through the synthetic maze. In either case, whether the reaction is programmed directly by the scientist's intelligence, or whether preplanned intelligence does the guiding, the mechanism of guidance is exactly the same—reaction conditions are altered, "roadblocks" are erected, and reaction pathways are "widened."

Even vastly simpler synthetic mazes, such as the synthesis of ascorbic acid, require information ("live" or "canned") for successful running. The inherent properties resident on the reactant are, alone, inadequate to achieve the desired exit point. *Why should we then imagine that life's infinitely more complex synthetic maze could be run successfully on less information than a simple ascorbic acid synthesis needs?*

In general, the scientific materialists admonish the supernaturalists to respect the physical and chemical laws which govern the behavior of matter. They are perfectly justified in doing so. But now the reverse is true; it is the supramaterialists who must admonish their scientific materialist colleagues to steadfastly respect the laws governing nature when they formulate their hypotheses and build their theories.

Scientists today know very well indeed that they must apply exogenous constraints and supply information to undergird the properties of matter if certain synthetic goals are to be reached. In fact, science has been injecting intelligence and intellectual effort on a stupendous scale into reaction systems in the hope of pulling out a living organism from an exit point in the maze. *But scientific materialism denies this very principle in its theories of the origin of life. That is, scientific materialism practices one thing—the principle of exogenous direction and information—but preaches another, especially when it comes to matters supernatural and religious. For it practices exogenous interference in things material in order to synthesize life in the laboratory, but denies exogenous interference at abiogenesis. In other words, the whole matter is reduced to an unwillingness to acknowledge exogenous interference of abiogenesis, even when all the scientific evidence demands that we acknowledge it.*

Before closing this section, perhaps one more illustration will be of interest. It deals with our stay in Turkey and so may be of cultural as well as scientific application.

AN ILLUSTRATION FROM THE NEAR EAST

Recently my wife and I were invited to a concert given by a group of young Turks interested in developing classical Western music in Ankara, Turkey. Anyone acquainted with national Turkish music, and indeed with any Oriental music, will realize how different are classical concepts of music in the East and in the West.

Our group of Turks gave a masterly and delightful interpretation of works of Handel and J. S. Bach. They performed on strings as well as on the harpsichord. It became rapidly clear that each of these young Turks was, by himself, perfectly capable of a solo performance of his particular part of the orchestral score. In fact, it might be said that each of our young musicians with his instrument possessed all the "inherent properties" to perform "autonomously" and skillfully the necessary musical reactions. But, musicians plus instruments plus musical scores do not necessarily produce accomplished orchestras! One other factor is vital. The musical "reaction" originating in the head and hands of each musician has to be presided over by a competent conductor who understands the whole score and can integrate each part into a unified piece of orchestral music. Similarly, many separate chemical reactions of life's metabolism are well understood and follow ordinary chemical laws. It is the *integrating* of the many separate chemical reactions of a cell into the one integrated whole of cellular and organismal metabolism which requires so much more understanding. The direction of the inherent capacities of these young Turks was in capable hands. Without him, less would have been achieved in the way of an integrated interpretation of what the composer intended. It is difficult for each musician to concentrate on playing his own instrument while at the same time concentrating on the scores of all the other musicians, and coordinating them.

As Kenyon himself at one time admitted, we do not know, nor can we imagine (that is to say, on the basis of scientific materialism alone) whatever made individual molecules and groups of reacting systems come together to function as a single metabolizing group or organism ("orchestra"). If we imagine a supersynthetic reaction maze which contains not one but thousands of separate maze pathways all interwined and all integrated and all leading to a whole known as a total metabolizing organism, then we have a faint picture of the degree of "orchestration" needed to establish and maintain life. The complexity of the "orchestration" of the metabolism of a human being is so inconceivably highly developed that it is almost infinitely complex to the human mind. The coding systems on the genes which have been elucidated to date bear witness to this fact.

In order to succeed, whatever supplies the information necessary to orchestrate biological metabolism must have a general overview of the whole metabolizing unit. To dismiss this problem as one of mere chance is simply unrealistic. To maintain that such a system could be developed if a few billion years were added to the equation to be solved is just as unrealistic, for the decomposition reactions in a system of such reduced entropy status would long since have caught up with the synthesis, and equilibrium would have been established, as Blum so well points out. To believe that the coding needed for such a fantastic piece of metabolic machinery is inherent in simple amino acid molecules is almost as good (or bad?) as believing in miracles! For, on genes we can at least examine the codes and work out the complex sequences.

That is, a basic mechanism for an adequate coding system is materially present and can be examined. However, there would not seem to be the slightest chance of an adequate coding mechanism being present on simple amino acids to cope with the fantastic order and orchestration of life's metabolism.

Let us be realistic. To coordinate ("orchestrate"), life's metabolism needs a fabulous coding order, and one must look for the material site of this coding to understand material metabolism. In the present state of knowledge, particularly of knowledge in the area of information theory, we dare not dismiss this problem of the site of coding and information with a shrug of the shoulders, mumbling something about inherent order on biomonomers, randomness and billions of years. Where order and coding are concerned, there must be a place for them. Genes offer such a site, but biomonomers do not.

This brings us to the final problem we have to face in the first section of this book: *Where must we look for an overall supplier of coded information to orchestrate the manifold aspects of abiogenesis and biological metabolism? The outworking of a most consummately complex coding system is plainly visible in life's metabolism. Where did the controlling code originate?*

FACING UP TO THE REAL PROBLEM

The fact is, of course, that, although many scientists recognize the necessity of sources of information, coding and reaction constraint in theories of abiogenesis and life's maintenance, *few will admit the bankruptcy of scientific materialism in these problems. Rather, scientific materialism is regularly preached as having solved most of life's problems without the necessity of appealing to the existence of a God. Therefore, so runs the propaganda line in the lecture rooms of the majority of the world's universities, to believe in the necessity of divine volition in accounting for the problems is to be laughably backward—indeed, unfit to teach at a uni-*

versity level.

However, though we have not proved the existence of God, we have shown that the materialist position knows of no better way to account for the coding behind life. The believer in the Divine does offer a solution, even though it is one that the materialist abhors. Further, as we shall see in Part II, this solution exactly fits the experimental result gained in the laboratory in this subject in recent years.

To go one step further, the scientific materialists are risking collision with the known laws of thermodynamics in persisting with their dislike of the solution the supranaturalist offers them. The irony of the situation is that the intense study of matter today has brought us to the position where we have to assume some sort of reality and direction outside (or pervading) matter. Why not admit to this state of affairs? The answer is, of course, that this would seem like putting the clock back, for belief in divine direction is allegedly outdated. We are forced to believe in extramaterial direction by the facts of nature and are therefore forced to conclude that scientific materialism has been barking up the wrong tree for over one hundred years. And now we must get back on the right track. In that sense, putting the clock back is the only sensible thing to do, for it is the same thing as getting back on the right (though ancient) track.

Why scientists should be unwilling to postulate an exogenous intelligence as responsible for the observed facts in nature is less understandable today than it was twenty years ago, in view of the advances in the knowledge of information theory and coding mechanisms. We must ask ourselves, then, why is there this basic objection in scientific circles to the postulate of exogenous direction and coding in accounting for the direction and coding of life when almost any other form of speculation is allowed? Perhaps it is the assumption of *an intelligence independent of and perhaps vastly superior to our own* which seems to be so unpalatable.

Our grandfathers are ridiculed for their naïve belief in an "old man in the sky," who was supposed to have synthesized everything, including humanity. This was the form of exogenous, extraterrestrial intelligence in which they allegedly believed. But, in those days, intelligence was indissolubly associated with humanity—or superhumanity—and therefore with the human brain, blood, proteins and, recently, with genes and DNA. It became rather ridiculous, as the meaning and function of human anatomy and physiology emerged, to believe in intelligence coupled to this type of physiology high up in space where there is no air for metabolism, no food to eat, and no waste-disposal systems! It was obviously "unscientific" to believe in an intelligence so indissolubly associated with a human physiology, and any who were naïve enough to credit the synthesis of the material universe and of life to the benign and fatherly deity with the white beard were the butt of scientific ridicule. Yet, when conceiving of exogenous intelligence, it was difficult to avoid this cul-de-sac in thought, for intelligence, fifty years ago, always had to be linked to human physiology and thought.

Perhaps it was this sort of reasoning that made modern science decide, at all costs, to do without the postulate of any intelligence exogenous to our own. But in banning the concept of the divine from scientific laboratories, scientific papers and seminars, scientists overlooked the treacherous scientific ground they now began to tread. *For the question of the ultimate origin of the order and codes behind life and matter, and the problem of the coding behind the order of life's building blocks guiding them through life's synthetic maze, as well as the question of the "orchestration" of the multitude of metabolic processes cannot be solved by banning the idea of a source of order of coding sequences, that is, of intelligence. The hard fact remains that all "programming" must originate in intelligence somewhere down the line.*

Therefore, we shall have to put aside our prejudices of the past hundred years or so and reexamine the whole question of an exogenous intelligence as responsible for life's original coding and synthetic maze-running operations. In fact, as things stand, we would expect to be able to characterize this intelligence a little. It must be mathematical in its mode of function. (At least, we might assume this, for its products are susceptible of mathematical treatment.) The same applies to the terms *chemical, physical* and *psychological,* for all these properties are inherent in the order we see in nature and therefore, presumably, must also have been present in their source.

Intense research is being conducted today in the area of artificial consciousness, and new light is being thrown on all these problems. It is possible to carry out projects on artificial intelligence and consciousness with much more ease and control today than it would have been twenty years ago. We now know that artificial intelligence can ride on transistors and thermionic tubes. Intelligence is no longer bound to hemoglobin and brain tissue as it used to be. This means that the idea of an exogenous intelligence, responsible for the order in and around us, is no longer coupled to the idea of a physiological deity in the sky, which has been such a hindrance to the consideration of the Divine in scientific circles. Today it is clear that intelligence can ride on purely electrical systems and does not need biology's aid in functioning. We shall look into the various types of synthetic intelligence available today together with the significance of experiments in which they are used. We must also examine the nature of consciousness itself, which is somewhat more difficult than the matter of intelligence alone.

Part II will concern itself with some of the elementary facts of artificial intelligence and artificial consciousness. The data gathered will then be applied to a synthesis on the origins, maintenance and meaning of life.

1. Dean H. Kenyon and Gary Steinman, *Biochemical Predestination*, p. 269.
2. Ibid., p. 268.
3. Ibid., p. 263.
4. Ibid., p. 265.
5. In P. S. Moorhead and M. M. Kaplan, eds., *Mathematical Challenges to the Neo-Darwinian Interpretation of Evolution*, p. 77.

PART 2

7.

relationships between speciation and metabolic energy

PROGRAMMING THE CELL: ENERGY CONSIDERATIONS

The laws of thermodynamics today present no difficulties in accounting for ontogenetical evolution. There are no difficulties of a thermodynamic nature in accounting for the huge decrease in entropy involved when a zygote (fertilized egg) develops to a fully grown adult organism. This increase in order is, thermodynamically, accountable for on the basis of prior *programming* on the DNA/RNA/ribosome systems present in the original zygote, and an adequate supply of coupled *energy,* derived from nutrient catabolism, to finance the complex robot known as the fertilized egg up to the adult state.

Thus, on the basis of these two points, the whole process of ontogenetical upward evolution can be relatively easily accounted for, even though the mechanisms involved are fantastically complex. For all ontogenetical development is attributable to preprogramming—just as sodium and chlorine ions are preprogrammed to form salt crystals under the correct conditions. Accordingly, the enormous complexity of the human brain (and other organs) is not to be accounted for on the basis of chance development as far as ontogeny is concerned. Rather it is to be referred to perfectly ordered coding systems which direct the whole development of the organ.

On the other hand, things are not so simple when it comes to accounting for the evolution of phylogeny. The general Neo-Darwinian position is that this development was not coded or programmed, but that chance and long time spans plus natural selection were the sources of this order. But the thermodynamic side of this position is much less clear than in the case of ontogenetic development. For the energy relationships and coding or programming arrangements are not immediately discernible in this scheme of things.

The energy provided for ontogenetical development was strictly defined—it came from easily definable coupled reaction systems which make up the process of metabolism. The coding was that which could be studied on genes and chromosomes. We find, in contrast to this clear position, much that is nebulous in the theory which attempts to account for phylogeny. The only coding that the Darwinians offer to account for the development of species in phylogeny is that offered by random reactions. And the only energy is random energy derived ultimately from the sun. For if the sun did not directly supply the energy for upward speciation, then it must have been derived indirectly from cellular energy in the course of metabolism.

Many scientists see little evidence that the cell could use its own metabolic energy to effect phylogenetic development. As we have already seen, development of any sort which requires increase in basic order (or decrease in entropy) must be energetically financed as well as thoroughly coded and programmed. This means that theoretical difficulties begin to arise only when new cellular development has to be accounted for in phylogeny without the necessary pre-coding. Once a cell's own programming and energy supply is established, its duplication, together with metabolism, presents no problems. What is lacking, however, in phylogenetical Darwinian evolution or speciation, is a means of supplying *new coding* for the entropy reduction necessary for upward speciation, together with an energy supply.

We have already discussed the appearance of coding and discuss it again later. Here we are concerned chiefly with the second part of the problem, namely, that of the *energy supply* for entropy reduction. For we must finance any new departures in cell structure by means of energy. Even programming itself, being a form of entropy reduction, must be energetically financed too, to say nothing of the outworking of programming in the growth of new cell structure and functions. Thus, the arising of new coding or programming systems, together with the working out of these programs, requires energetic financing which, in the general type of Neo-Darwinian theory current today, is inadequately accounted for.

The problem can be clarified by turning to the science of robot construction. It is possible today to design a robot which will behave in certain clearly defined ways. If energy is supplied, the robot will stand up, sit down, advance (somewhat clumsily), greet a newcomer, and perhaps even answer simple questions. It might be possible to develop a robot which can effect minor repairs on itself. Robots which seek their own energy supplies—electrical outlets placed at intervals in laboratory walls—have been designed and constructed. Such machines convert their "metabolic" energy into preprogrammed action. They are to be compared with a biological cell which can carry on its own metabolism under the correct energetic conditions.

Difficulties begin to arise, however, when we take a step further and ask ourselves whether it would be possible to construct a robot so that it could not only carry out its preprogrammed actions, but could also use a portion of its "metabolic energy" (with which it is supplied from wall outlets) to develop itself upward toward a bigger and better robot. Could robots be designed which would gradually perfect themselves by diverting at least a part of the energy available to them for their own upward programming, upward coding, and upward evolution? This is a vastly more difficult problem than that of programming a robot to say good morning when someone enters the laboratory. But it is a problem which is being solved in learning machines.

There is no difficulty in principle about the fact that a cell is *programmed* to grow to adulthood by using its *own metabolic energy to effect entropy reduction*. There is a query, however, about the proposal that a cell could divert some of its own metabolic energy to finance its own upward reduction of entropy *in upward speciation or evolution*. A cell can, obviously, use its metabolic energy to work out its own *inherent programming*. But can it use its own metabolic energy to "better" its own programming, that is, to develop upward, specieswise, in the evolutionary sense of the word?

Again, *replication* in an already totally programmed cell or robot *presents no problems* so long as suitable energy is available to realize the program. The difficulties begin when the problem of *upward coding* is attacked, that is, when upward evolution, or speciation, is considered. This means that we must search for a scheme which would provide the robot (or cell) with a means of self-evolution and therefore of upward coding duly financed by its own metabolic energy, if we would have cells or robots which are to continually develop into bigger, better and more intelligent cells and robots. Accordingly, we must look now into the programming of cells and robots for self-improvement, for that is the basic problem of all upward speciation and evolution.

METABOLIC ENERGY, PROGRAMMING
AND INTELLIGENCE

To elucidate this vital problem we must first ask ourselves the following question: Is there, in our present experience, any *theoretical* possibility of putting our own human, cellular, metabolic energy to work so as to finance any sort of upward evolution or upward programming? We know that learning machines can do this feat.

The answer to this question must be, in our own case at least, in the affirmative. For our own nervous system is capable of using our own metabolic energy to improve multitudes of programs both inside and outside the biological sphere. Our brain is active in reducing, for example, the entropy of iron ore or bauxite to produce not only iron and aluminum but also locomotives and airplanes. These activities involve entropy reduction (program production) at the expense of energy. The programming inherent in such activities is very considerable indeed. *Thus, the brain is remarkable in that it is capable of developing the new, coded programs on the basis of the energy it gains from our human metabolism.*

In summary, we can therefore maintain that the brain is a converter of metabolic calories into codes, programs, nervous energy or intelligence. The exact mechanism by which this conversion of calories into programs and codes is achieved is under intensive investigation today. However, even though the precise mechanisms by which this conversion of calories into programs is achieved are not yet fully known, the ability of the central nervous system to perform this feat has been exploited practically for thousands of years in human history and prehistory. *Indeed, our civilizations and cultures through all time have depended upon this process—the conversion of potatoes, proteins and pudding into ideas and intelligence which end up as new programs for engineering, building, manufacturing, creative art, writing and music.*

This process of converting calories into programs extends, of course, beyond the human central nervous system into the higher regions of the animal kingdom—and perhaps, to a small extent at least, into some odd corners of the plant kingdom too, though nervous tissue in a specialized plant form is conspicuous by its absence. Birds build their nests (probably preprogrammed, admittedly), monkeys and apes make primitive tools and develop new approaches to this activity, rabbits excavate their burrows, spiders spin their webs. Much of this activity in the animal kingdom may be attributed to the working out of programs already inherent upon genetic material. But there is evidence that, in some cases, new ideas or programs may perhaps be worked out in the animal kingdom as a result of the conversion of calories into ideas and programs. This is particularly true among the higher primates.

Obviously, then, in the biological world, the development of new programs is, in general, dependent upon the ability of the central nervous system to convert the increase of entropy resulting from the metabolizing of food into the reduction of entropy embodied in the conception of new programs and codes. *This ability of certain specialized organs in the biological world to convert calories into ideas and programs, this linking of calories with codes, is an important subject which has, we believe, been overlooked by some abiogenetic theory makers. It is obviously an essential bridge in the development of any theories concerned with biological programming, for it alone supplies a theoretical basis for the appearance and evolution of coding programs in general.* As we have so often insisted, randomness offers no satisfactory theoretical solution for coding and programming. We could, however, account for upward programming if we could link supplies of energy to programming in some way. *The central nervous system is the only biological organ known which can establish this link.*

By making use of this link and developing the idea behind it, we hope to be able to put evolutionary theory in general and speciation in particular on a sound thermodynamic basis which no appeal to chance, long time spans and natural selection or even biochemical predestination has been able to achieve.

THE BRAIN AS A CONVERTER OF CALORIES INTO CODES

Up to the present it has been possible to employ human intelligence (as opposed to animal intelligence) for upward programming chiefly in matters exogenous to man himself. Man has improved the genetic programming of animals and plants in a most impressive manner. He has shown himself able to employ his metabolic calories via the medium of his central nervous system in the critical selection of breeding strains and types to ensure products which are improvements on previous types. This process of upward coding in plants and animals is a direct result of new ideas financed from man's available calories. The reductions in entropy achieved are, theoretically, well-financed reductions and present no theoretical difficulties at all.

In exactly the same way man has successfully used his calorie-consuming brain to finance the programming of factories, homes, ballistic missiles, computers, information retrieval systems, etc. There is no chance or randomness about all this. Everything is based upon sound thermodynamic principles. The new ideas, codes and programs are all energetically accountable for. The achievement of modern civilization with its conveniences is all squarely based upon man's brain and its ability to convert at least a portion of the calorific energy derived from potatoes and proteins into nervous energy, intelligence, coding, programs and ideas. These are the prime movers behind man's activities. It is they which make him so different from animals in general. One cannot overemphasize this point—that *the brain*, the converter of calories into codes and intelligence, *is always the vital link in any schemes involving upward programming, or evolution.*

Having established this point, we must now take one more step in the development of the calorie-to-code idea.

A NEW AND HITHERTO UNPRECEDENTED STEP

In recent years man has begun to take a new and hitherto unprecedented step in his use of calorie-financed nervous energy or coding ability. *He is planning to make his first attempts at genetic surgery in plants and animals with a view, eventually, to inserting new programs and new codes into their very genetic sequences and codes.* When he understands the chemical sequences and meaning behind the DNA codes, and knows just what each is responsible for, man intends to alter these codes so as to improve the animal and plant organisms concerned. By using his own coding and ideas, man intends to up-program and up-code certain plants and animals for his own purposes. This new method is not the same as the old one which only involved reshuffling and resorting the genetic codings already on hand. *It involves making new codes, not merely recombining old ones.* This genetic surgery really represents upward evolution *par excellence.*

When this work has succeeded in plants and animals, the possibility of applying the same recoding and up-coding of man himself lies open. Man is hoping to use his own metabolic calories to supply the intelligent force or coding needed to reprogram himself, as well as other organisms. *Man is on the way, that is, to becoming like a robot which knows how to use his own metabolic energy to re-program himself upward.*

What does all this imply? Surely that man has found a better way to achieve upward programming than that which involved chance, long time spans and natural selection and is getting down to the root of the technique in attacking the very code-bearers of life, the genes. This is a much faster and infinitely more accurate way, theoretically speaking. Besides this, the selection and reshuffling of genes which are already on hand are much less fruitful than *making new genes, codes and programs.* The following example will underscore this aspect.

EXPERIMENTS IN THE UPWARD
EVOLUTION OF THE SUGAR BEET

In the first half of the nineteenth century the sugar content of the sugar beet was raised by selective breeding (gene sorting and reshuffling) by well over 50 percent of its original value, to some 17 percent of sugar by weight. Although intensive breeding and selection experiments have continued over the years, little further improvement in sugar content has been achieved. The limits set by gene makeup and breeding selection have been reached, and no amount of even highly intelligent breeding selection and reshuffling has helped toward further upward evolution. Apparently further improvement in sugar content is not inherent on the gene programming. If improvement is not inherent on the genes, of course, it cannot be brought out by further reshuffling.

On the other hand, if the structure of the genes and their inherent chemistry and sequences were so well known and understood that the hidden chemical factors controlling sugar concentration were clear, then one might be able to alter the sequences and coding on the genes which control sugar concentration so that they could undergo still further improvement. New genetic factors could be *created* by genetic surgery which would break through and go beyond the present barrier of about 17 percent sugar concentration.

All this means that the old limits set by gene reshuffling have been shattered—at least in theory. Upward programming can now be envisaged on a scale hitherto unthought of. For, by means of genetic chemical surgery, entirely new structures, species and types could be coded into the germ plasm. *Evolution by upward programming is now on the horizon, although it has not yet been realized.*

However, the old method of securing new strains by selection and recombination was relatively elementary in concept and the technique was therefore quite simple. One merely sorted out from the results of selected breeding pairs those individuals bearing the properties sought for, and then bred from them. The intellectual effort required and the knowledge involved were of an order easily grasped by a large number of individuals with a normal central nervous system! But a different order of intellectual effort will have to be envisaged to realize the feats of chemical understanding and manipulation which will guide chemico-genetic surgery to insert new coding into the germ plasm.

What we wish to bring out here is that the intellectual programming "energy" needed for upgrading of coding by chemico-genetic surgery is vastly greater than that involved in the older sorting methods which involved only recombinations and reshufflings. We should not look down on older methods—they have done wonders in the analysis and synthesis of genetic problems and have produced marvelous results. Nevertheless, the pure knowledge and manipulative skill required for chemico-genetic surgery must be of a quite different order compared with older methods. Even in research there is a strong upward evolution in techniques and manipulation! Might we say that "low power" intellectual force was used in the past, whereas today "high power" nervous energy is needed to insert the newly created codes after discovering them?

The main point which we have been establishing is *that true upward evolution is dependent upon true upward coding, and that true upward coding cannot come from randomness but at present only from the conversion of calories into codes through the mediation of that unique organ we call the central nervous system.*

Learning machines are catching up with this ability of the brain. This brings us to the question of the uniqueness of the brain and its functions. For it will be obvious that, *if the brain were the only organ capable of producing codes and thought, then we would have no way of accounting for codes and thought before the brain arose.* The question is, then, whether the brain is, in its functions, unique.

THE UNIQUENESS OF THE BRAIN AS A CODING ORGAN

The nervous systems of both man and the higher animals were, until recently, the only mechanisms known to have experimentally demonstrated their ability to produce such proofs of thought as shown by the ability to learn and the production of codes. There is nothing mysterious about this, for these biological processes are calorie-financed, as we have seen. All the same, the observation that calories and energy can be put to work to make codes and programs, supplies—as already hinted—a vital bridge to span the gap noted by Schützenberger and others in present Neo-Darwinian theory. These scientists made it clear that randomness concepts coupled with long time spans will never account for the codes of which material life consists. We recall that Eden expressed himself on this point as follows:

> It is our contention that if "random" is given a serious and crucial interpretation from a probabilitistic point of view, the randomness postulate is highly implausible and that an adequate scientific theory of evolution must await the discovery and elucidation of new natural laws.[1]

Now, if the central nervous system is capable of converting metabolic energy into intellectual and coding forces capable of arranging programs out of nonprograms; if it is capable of reducing entropy and of financing that reduction by increasing the entropy of food molecules, *then the "discovery and elucidation of new natural laws," which Eden requires to explain evolution and upcoding, are no longer necessary.* For here we have an organ which, in principle, is capable of adequately accounting for the coding order and its development which we see in life and nature around us. *All we need to account for all nature's order is a bigger and better organ, functioning on the same principles as the brain, but in a much more extensive way.* New natural laws are certainly not necessary—we need only extrapolation of the laws governing the functioning of the brain as we know it and with which we can and do experiment.

The facts of physics and the second law of thermodynamics both demand that codes and programs be made and realized at the expense of energy. There does not appear to be any other principle upon which one can build up any theory accounting for codes and order. But simple irradiation of matter with solar energy (or any other energy, for that matter) will not produce codes. Again, as we have seen so often in other problems, a metabolic motor must be utilized to extract the order from randomness. The central nervous system is the one motor organ which can and does extract codes, plans, programs and intellectual forces, by metabolism, from protein and potatoes. *Using such an organ, we can account for the appearance of order from nonorder without invoking any of Eden's "new natural laws." Here we have the missing natural law, but it is not new!*

The difficulty in digesting this state of affairs has always arisen when the next question is asked. In fact, it is probable that this question has scared off many speculators from following further the logic of this evolution of thought. The question is an obvious one: Where did the intellectual force necessary to account for the order of matter and life's codes come from? For most of nature's codes arose before man and his brain arrived. We have established the principle that codes and programs cost energy and that the biological central nervous system is a unique organ possessing the faculty of converting energy into such programs and codes. Have we any reason to believe that such a thought organ existed and produced the order and programs we see in life and the universe *before* the human and other biological thought organs arose?

The evidence is very strong indeed that such thought organs must have been extant and preexistent in order to conceive the codes we see in matter and life. Mathematicians and physicists such as Sir James Jeans have long maintained that the universe resembles a universe of thought or intellectual programming force which showed its action and presence in matter and life codes. After all, it is true that all scientists, no matter what their *Weltanschauung,* believe the same, even though some will not admit it. *For they all believe that nature is based on law, that is, on codes and order. Their life efforts are devoted to exposing and understanding these basic laws, orders and codes in nature.* It would be unthinkable for a scientist to declare that he did not believe in codes, law and order behind nature. We must therefore repeat *that the only source of law, order, codes and programs which we know about experimentally is a thought organ (like the brain) which converts calories into codes and order.*

Is it possible to conceive of such an organ before man, matter or biology arose? The answer which modern cybernetic sciences are giving us more clearly every day is that *we certainly can conceive of such an intelligent force, acting entirely independently of biology as we know it.*

THOUGHT EXOGENOUS TO BIOLOGY— SOME INTELLECTUAL DIFFICULTIES

Modern man, with some notable exceptions, has become unwilling to accept the view that an intelligence exogenous to his own is responsible for himself or the order around him. The principles of the proposition of exogenous intelligence may be all right for most scientists, but the practical application of such a concept lies too near to the old idea of Deity to be acceptable to most. But, if the reasons for this inherent unwillingness to accept the idea of an exogenous intelligence behind the codes of nature could be exposed and removed, there might be less difficulty in accepting the basic principles we have suggested to account for nature's programming.

No doubt one of the basic reasons for the scientific rejection of the idea of any intelligence exogenous to our own is the shocking record of depravity and cruelty that belief in Deity, or religion of any sort, has shown in the world's history from earliest times on. Scientists have been unwilling to associate themselves with a belief with such a bad record. But, as we have already pointed out, man's basic record in history has not been too good, no matter what belief or unbelief, atheistic or deistic, he has embraced, so that the bad record associated with religion may be due, not so much to religion itself, as to its combination with the vagaries of human nature.

Perhaps a second reason for this basic unwillingness to believe in any deity can be associated with the fact that it is the *primitive* people who have seen God in everything, bad or good. As they progressed they "grew out of" this belief and learned how to predict drought, famine, plague, thunder, lightning, hail and snow (the "divine" manifestations). A continuation of this "progress" seems to have led to the total elimination of all belief in the Divine. Scientists naturally dissociate themselves from crude, primitive beliefs.

A third reason for unwillingness to accept the above thesis is perhaps that man is used to being regarded as the only rational being and certainly the most intelligent of all biological beings. He does not take kindly to the idea of losing his lofty throne in intellectual areas. If there is an intelligence vastly superior to man's, it is unlikely that man's relatively puny intelligence will be able to cope or experiment with such vast intellectual resources. Man, in these democratic days, does not like the idea of falling at anyone's feet as an intellectual inferior. We cling to the idealistic notion that we are all born equal, and extrapolate it beyond man.

Last, man for the past few centuries has seen little of "miraculous" phenomena which could be unequivocally attributed to the Divine in nature. Miracles are rare events, seen by few, and often unverifiable, so that old miracles reportedly due to divine intervention are believed by few today. Scientists and intellectuals do not wish to be associated with the credulous.

It is therefore regarded as "progressive" not to believe in anything smacking of divine intelligence as an answer to life's coding and programming problems. However, since none of the reasons given above as objections to exogenous intelligence are such that one could build a scientific theory on them, we are forced back to the basic proposition again: Mathematicians and scientists are showing that merely discrediting belief in an exogenous intelligence will never solve our basic scientific problem. For the hard facts remain. Energy and entropy relationships *must be accounted for* when dealing with programs and codes.

However, the postulate of a programming organ working in a parallel but infinitely larger way to our own central nervous system, does, in principle, offer hope of a solution. The idea would find immediate reception among many experimental scientists because they can conclude from experience that order and programs do arise in this manner, if only the odium of "religion" could be removed from the concept. Things would then be so much simpler for many. Many of the more intelligent and intellectually minded simply cannot accept the sometimes crude ideas of the "old man in the sky" usually associated with the supreme-intelligence postulate.

It is our thesis that these genuine hindrances to accepting the postulate of an exogenous intelligence to account for nature's coding have been finally and completely overcome by quite recent advances in cybernetic science. The difficulties of the anthropomorphism which has been such a hindrance to all ideas of exogenous intelligence have been banished. It is our purpose to demonstrate these points in elaborating on progress in knowledge of the nature of both artificial intelligence and artificial consciousness.

It will be necessary, therefore, to develop the postulate of an exogenous programmer in the light of recently gained knowledge on artificial intelligence and consciousness. *For it is now known that both intelligence, and probably consciousness, can theoretically exist independently of biology, and of man.* Such artificially induced intelligence rides on electronic gear, and it needs no anthropomorphology to explain it. In short, artificial intelligence puts energy, coding, programming and patterns, as we see them in life, matter, speciation and evolution, on a sound thermodynamic basis without any appeal to biology or to the "new natural laws" to which Murray Eden wished to resort in his attempt to put Neo-Darwinism on a rational basis.

Accordingly, the next chapters deal with questions involving artificial consciousness and intelligence.

1. M. Eden, article in P. S. Moorhead and M. M. Kaplan, eds., *Mathematical Challenges to the Neo-Darwinian Interpretation of Evolution*, p. 109.

artificial
consciousness

CULBERTSON'S WORK

In 1963 James T. Culbertson published a book, the main purpose of which was to show in detail how states of consciousness could be artificially produced, that is, how consciousness could arise in artificially constructed devices, or in robots.[1] He proceeds from the viewpoint that states of consciousness are feelings of pain, color experiences, sensations of sound, taste and smell, and that when any human, animal or robot has such mental experiences, perceptions or memory images, consciousness exists.[2]

Consciousness is to be very carefully distinguished from behavior. If, for example, one steps on a dog's tail, the dog jumps up and yelps because it is highly conscious of the pain, thus giving vent to its "feelings." Its jumping up and barking are the behaviors coupled, in this case, with the dog's consciousness of pain.

On the other hand, a robot dog might be designed, constructed and programmed in such a manner that when its tail is stepped on, it, too, jumps up and barks. That is, the robot would closely simulate the biological dog in its behavior patterns. But his does not mean that the robot dog would actually be conscious of the pain in its tail. The robot dog may, in fact, not be designed to be conscious at all, even though its behavior is, outwardly speaking, fully canine. In the robot dog, behavior and consciousness are not coupled, there being no consciousness to which behavior could be coupled.

There is a third possibility. A dog might be fully conscious and at the same time be so completely paralyzed that it would show no externally detectable behavior at all. It would not even be able to move. Here the dog possesses consciousness which is not coupled to behavior on account of the total paralysis. But, even without detectable behavior, the animal may be very conscious indeed.

In this connection the case of an ex-soldier, who was once brought to my notice, comes to mind. The poor man had been so badly shattered in an explosion during World War I that not only was his hearing, sight and sense of smell almost totally destroyed, but all his limbs had been blown off, leaving only the stumps. In addition, he was incapable of anything but the slightest movements of his head or body. In short, he was unable to exhibit much behavior at all. The motor mechanisms of the body, which are the normal outlets of consciousness, were almost totally lacking. However, by perseveringly developing a tactile code which some friends had worked out with him, this crippled soldier was able to indicate that, inwardly, in his consciousness, he was still a perfectly normal man with many of the desires, delights, pains and sorrows of a normal person possessing the usual behavioral outlets for consciousness. Although his consciousness was only tenuously coupled to behavior, it was in no way impaired.

Thus states of consciousness are subjective experiences of sensations, impressions, ideas or sensa, but these states are not necessarily coupled to external behavior. This can be illustrated by mention of the effect of substances such as succinyl choline or curare on the body. Such drugs can completely paralyze muscular tissue so that a patient under their influence is unable to bat an eyelid. Yet consciousness is in no way impaired. It has happened that, through an error of medication, a patient has been operated on while fully conscious but completely unable to communicate his predicament to the surgeon. One patient reporting such an experience was a medical man who afterward sought to warn anesthetists of the horrors of such a situation. Curare and succinyl choline are, accordingly, excellent decouplers of behavior and consciousness. It is evident, therefore, that *behavior is not necessarily an index of consciousness,* so that the two states must be carefully distinguished in our theories on these subjects. "Intelligent" behavior may not necessarily indicate an "intelligent" consciousness.

Culbertson considers consciousness to be made up of two components: (1) sense data arising from perception via the sense organs, and (2) "memory images," which he regards as mediated by neurons in "memory box" circuits.[3] He then proceeds to demonstrate that "sense data and memory images can be produced in automata consisting of artificial neurons connected together in certain ways."[4]

If this is truly the case, then artificial consciousness could be synthesized in certain electronic circuitry. Culbertson puts it this way:

> Artificial consciousness, i.e., experience of subjective phenomena produced by sending impulses through artificial nerve nets, may employ very different devices from those needed in animals or men. . . . Consciousness (subjective phenomena, sense data, memory images, etc.) can be constructed in non-biological materials.[4]

Culbertson then goes on to develop this theory. Since his conclusions are relevant to our examination of artificial consciousness and artificial intelligence, we must look into them, even if only very briefly.

THE NERVE NET THEORY OF SENSE
DATA AND CONSCIOUSNESS

Consistent with the above hypothesis, Culbertson devotes the second part of his book to developing the nerve net theory of sense data and consciousness. The concept has little to do with the idea behind behavior in any contemporary robots, machinery or computers, for, as we have already seen, consciousness may or may not accompany their behavior. Contemporary robots are constructed to exhibit behavior but not to experience consciousness.

For Culbertson, consciousness accompanies any machine (or neural biological) activity in which impulses are connected together while passing through the machine or neural network. The consciousness produced by this means, in contemporary electronic machines such as computers, is, in Culbertson's view, so trivial and negligible that it can be entirely discounted. However, our author believes that suitably constructed automata could experience complex associations of sense data and memory images, both features of human consciousness. To experience such would, in Culbertson's view, be merely a question of designing the correct circuitry to produce this effect.[5]

These and other reasons led Culbertson to the belief that since consciousness accompanies brain activity,

> anyone believing that the brain is a machine or natural cause-effect mechanism of some kind should have no difficulty in accepting the preliminary working hypothesis that consciousness would accompany the activity of artificial machinery that was sufficiently similar to the brain in its structure.[6]

Accordingly, throughout Culbertson's work it is assumed that the brain is merely a machine and nothing else. Culbertson explains that he believes that there is nothing supernatural or superphysical about this organ. In making this assumption, Culbertson is assuming that thought itself, in being a product of matter alone, is in a sense a derivative of matter.

Thus Culbertson's line of thought fits into the general scientific materialistic scheme of things. We must analyze this attitude toward brain function just as we have analyzed other aspects of scientific materialism. We are convinced that the scientific materialistic interpretation of the brain, like its interpretation of evolution, is all right as far as it goes. But in both cases it is inadequate in that it leaves out evidence which is vital to give us the total picture of the problems it sets out to solve. Our next section investigates these matters.

C. D. BROAD'S WORK ON
BRAIN FUNCTION AND CONSCIOUSNESS

In taking this line of thought, Culbertson is omitting the evidence contrary to this view that the brain is solely a cause-and-effect machine. C. D. Broad, of Cambridge University, England, the well-known professor and researcher of psychiatric and supranatural phenomena, has spent a lifetime gathering and documenting evidence which does not line up with the materialist position, especially in matters of brain function. That Culbertson was unaware of this evidence seems unlikely since he quotes Broad on various occasions.[7]

Broad has spent a lifetime gathering and publishing evidence for precisely the position which Culbertson ignores in considering the nature of the brain and of consciousness itself. He points out that, although the brain is doubtless a physiological organ functioning according to the laws of biochemistry and physiology, it does exhibit psychic phenomena which are well defined and documented but which cannot be explained on the basis of any known mechanistic, chemical or physical laws.[8] We have cited a good deal of this evidence and added some of our own in *The Drug Users,* so that it is superfluous to requote it here.

In dealing with the matter of consciousness on this basis, Culbertson is, in fact, begging the question. First he assumes that it is possible to regard the brain as a mere cause-effect machine with nothing supraphysiological about it. This assumption then becomes the basis of his dogma that, if one builds a machine with physical circuitry similar to that of the brain, it will function exactly like a brain, even to the extent of consciousness. The whole piece of logic is a classical example of circular reasoning: the brain is first *assumed* to be a mere machine possessing no supraphysical properties, but exhibiting consciousness; on this basis the second assumption is then made, that if one constructs such a machine, it must exhibit consciousness. One might as well maintain that cake forms are associated with cakes; if, therefore, one constructs an artificial cake form it will automatically be cake through and through.

On the other hand, if the brain is an organ which is capable of receiving from and transmitting to a supraphysical sphere; if it possesses a psychic activity which is not explicable on the basis of known physical laws, then its psychic properties may not arise in itself, but may be merely mediated by it. In this sense, if consciousness is a purely psychic phenomenon— we are not maintaining that it is, for there is much discussion on this point—then a machine constructed on exactly the same basis as the brain might or might not show the same psychic properties and even consciousness. An illustration may help to make this possibility clearer.

INHERENT PROGRAMMING:
THE BRAIN VS. THE TELEVISION SET

Let us assume that I possess a television set which at this moment is transmitting a production of Shakespeare's *Hamlet*. We may say, out of deference to Culbertson, that the set is "experiencing" *Hamlet*. But dare we maintain that the television set screen is actually "conscious" of Shakespeare's *Hamlet*? For Culbertson seems to believe something like this, as we shall see later.

While the set is reproducing the scenes from *Hamlet*, I make an exact mechanical copy of the set's circuitry. My replica set, being complete after a few hours' work, is now turned on in the expectation that I not only possess an exact copy of the set, but also of its exact program at the time I made the replica of it. I am disappointed, for, when I turn on my new set as well as the original set, I find both sets giving a program which shows no resemblance to *Hamlet*. In fact, the two sets may be turned to different stations, and so each may show a different program. The fact that neither of them shows the original *Hamlet* program demonstrates that neither of them possesses an internally coded program. If both sets showed the identical program every time they were turned on (but one which varied from hour to hour), we would say they were receiving it from outside and we would be right. But, if they showed the same old program each time we turned either of them on, the way a jukebox does, then the evidence would be conclusive that the program was internally re-corded. In the first case the sets were not programmed inher-ently for the programs they gave. In the second case they were.

The human brain succeeds in falling between these two extremes. In certain ways all brains are programmed alike and in certain ways they certainly are not. If one studies the world patent literature, for example, there seem to be certain generalized yet significant thought trends which show that brains the world over are interested at the same time in simi-lar programs. Anyone who does research and publishes scien-tific papers knows the anxiety a scientist experiences. Some-one else may publish his significant finding before he can!

The "program" trend in the human brain is not that of the jukebox type. Today's program is different from yesterday's. There is a program trend showing changes from day to day as though a general trend in knowledge was being received by a multitude of brains tuned to the same sort of wavelength. We have discussed this ill-defined question elsewhere under the title of Mind-at-Large. Other scientists have also noted this.[9]

If the above generalized gropings have some substance be-hind them, they would help to explain other phenomena such as ESP and telepathy. It is, of course, perfectly plain that the very mention of these two subjects will be like the proverbial red flag to the bull in some quarters. I used to react in a similar way myself until some evidence came my way quite by accident, and indeed quite unsolicited and unwanted.

Thus, it is clear that a great deal of the brain's physiology and pharmacology can be perfectly satisfactorily explained on the basis of known laws which lie well within the sphere of inherent programming and scientific materialism. But it would be a brave man who would deny *all* the evidence which C. D. Broad and others cite to the effect that not *everything* concerning the behavior of the brain can be explained within this material spectrum. As we have tried to show elsewhere,[9] the subject of consciousness lies within this area of the extramaterial attributes of the brain.

FURTHER ASPECTS OF CULBERTSON'S VIEWS ON CONSCIOUSNESS

We must look further into Culbertson's views on consciousness for two reasons. First, they represent a reasonable cross section of views generally held in scientific materialist circles today. Second, they demonstrate the inadequacy of the materialist standpoint in this area.

In his efforts at explaining consciousness on a purely mechanical and therefore materialistic basis, Culbertson attempts to show that, if one succeeded in projecting mechanically in nerve trees (that is, nerve nets connected together in such a way that nerve impulses pass through the net in time as well as space) a three-dimensional/time graph image would result. This would not only be the case if the nerve trees were of biological origin. The same three-dimensional/time graphs in the same image form would have formed in artificial nerve nets through which the same electrical impulses were passed.

Culbertson is saying that if in our time/space habitat an event occurs, such as a dog chasing a cat, for example, and if an image of this exogenous event can be reproduced, not in actual substance, but in the form of an electron code of impulses in the nerve net or artificial circuitry, then that nerve net or circuit can be said to be *conscious* of the dog chasing the cat. Culbertson is maintaining that, if exogenous events taking place in physical space/time around about us can be reproduced in the psychospace—that is in the space/time area within the nerve nets of the brain—of the central nervous system, then that central nervous system becomes automatically conscious of the external event as it is being reproduced internally in the psychospace.

The mechanically reproduced three-dimensional/time image, which is electronically duplicated in code form in the neural trees of the brain or in the synthetic circuitry of a machine, confers, according to Culbertson, experiential consciousness of the image. If we can produce within the psychospace of the brain or machine a moving picture in electronic code form, then that psychospace may be said to be conscious of the image. This, in essence, is the basis of consciousness as conceived by Culbertson and others. It will be remarked that the whole concept is basically mechanical and includes not only the interpretation of consciousness with respect to outward events, but also with respect to memory images, imagination and thought itself.

Since these views are of such a wide spectrum in explaining brain function and consciousness itself, we shall have to examine their adequacy. The fact that the views propounded offer a purely mechanical explanation of thought and consciousness makes them attractive to some materialists but suspect in the eyes of many mathematical physicists.

THE INADEQUACY OF PURELY MECHANICAL CONCEPTS OF CONSCIOUSNESS

Culbertson maintains that if one succeeds in projecting an internal image of outside events onto a "screen" capable of receiving a three-dimensional/time image, then that screen will be conscious of the event projected onto it. That is, if an internal psychospace screen can be made to receive an external event in a suitably coded form, then that psychospace will become conscious of the external event.

A little reflection will show the inadequacy of this hypothesis. A two-dimensional/time image in photons can easily be projected onto a screen as a moving-picture image. Simulations of stereoscopic, three-dimensional/time events have been projected onto screens capable of receiving three-dimensional/time images. Such devices as steam banks have been used for this purpose. Various types of screens can receive various types of images. But surely there would be just as little justification for the assumption that these two- or three-dimensional/time images produce a consciousness of those images in the screen receiving them as there would be grounds for Culbertson's assertion that consciousness arises if one projects a three-dimensional/time image in electronic impulses onto a psychospace. No one is going to be easily convinced that, if one projects an image in photons (or electrons) onto a television or other screen, that screen is going to be conscious of the image projected.

It does not really matter whether the screen is capable of receiving a two-dimensional or a three-dimensional/time image. Neither does it matter whether the image is projected in a psychospace or not. To imagine that the mere projection of an image will produce consciousness of the same is surely a vast oversimplification of the problem. Obviously, if any psychospace is going to be conscious of any event, that event must be *first* projected onto it in as clearly defined a form as possible. But having the image in the psychospace is one problem. The other problem is: How does the psychospace or other screen receiving the space/time image become conscious of the data appearing on it? Though the technicalities of projecting the image on the psychospace screen are great, Culbertson's ingenuity suggests solutions. However, why should we get so involved in the technicalities of *projecting* an image in electron impulses onto a three-dimensional/time psychospace when we have yet to solve the real problem: *How does the psychospace interpret these impulses and to what does it report the substance of the image projected?* Here Culbertson's theories beg the question as to the nature of consciousness.

Technology today has mastered the art of projecting images onto paper, fluorescent screens, television screens, radar screens, etc. *But how to make the screen itself conscious of the image it carries is an entirely different—and much more difficult—problem, and one which should not be ignored because we are concentrating on the technicalities of the first problem.*

SIR JAMES JEANS AND THE PROBLEM OF CONSCIOUSNESS

It will be evident that Culbertson's concept of consciousness is yet another example of a purely mechanistic, materialistic interpretation of life. Many highly qualified scientists have repeatedly warned against this kind of superficiality and the shortsightedness which accompanies this oversimplified *Weltanschauung*.

Sir James Jeans is one scientist who has often pointed out the fallacy of purely mechanistic interpretations. Here is one of his better-known statements on the problem of oversimplification carried out in the interests of scientific materialism:

> The efforts of our nearest ancestors to interpret nature on engineering [i.e., mechanistic] lines proved equally inadequate. Nature has refused to accommodate herself to either of these man-made moulds. On the other hand, our efforts to interpret nature in terms of the concepts of pure mathematics have, so far, proved brilliantly successful. It would now seem to be beyond dispute that in some way nature is more closely allied to the concepts of pure mathematics than to those of biology or of engineering, and even if the mathematical interpretation is only a third man-made mould, it at least fits nature incomparably better than the two previously tried. . . . To my mind, the laws which nature obeys are less suggestive of those which a machine obeys in its motion than of those which a musician obeys in writing a fugue, or a poet in composing a sonnet. The motions of electrons and atoms do not resemble those of the parts of a locomotive so much as those of the dancers in a cotillion.[10]

Our point is that to explain anything so abstruse as thought, intelligence or consciousness on a purely mechanistic framework is a retrograde step in the formulation of scientific theory. *The history of scientific progress in the past thirty years or so has demonstrated that purely mechanistic explanations of reality are usually unsatisfactory in that they represent only a part or one side of the truth.*

We may therefore conclude that the answer to the problem of consciousness does not lie in the assumption that matter can mechanically produce or even bear the phenomenon of thought or consciousness. *In fact, the evidence for the exact reverse is quite strong. For matter itself was produced and is maintained by a process of thought. One can express this concept better by maintaining that thought is not the result of matter but that it (matter) is more probably the result of thought.*

Sir James Jeans is once more helpful in this problem: "If all this is so, then the universe can best be pictured, although still very imperfectly and inadequately, as consisting of pure thought, the thought of what, for want of a wider word, we must describe as a mathematical thinker."[11]

This idea of thought, consciousness and intellectual energy, rather than mere mechanics, as being the fundamental creative force of the universe has been developed further by Jeans, as the two following citations testify:

> We can also see why *energy, the fundamental entity of the universe,* had again to be treated as a mathematical abstraction—the constant of integration of a differential equation. The same concept implies of course that the final truth about a phenomenon resides in the mathematical description of it. . . . The making of models or pictures to explain mathematical formulae and the phenomena they describe, is not a step towards, but a step away from, reality; *it is like making graven images of a spirit.*[12]

Here Jeans points out that over sixty years ago scientists thought that we were heading for the discovery that ultimate reality was something of a mechanical entity. Life was thought to have stumbled blindly into the chemical and mechanical forces of a jumble of chaotic atoms and then to have evolved upward by the mechanistic action of natural selection and random mutation. Purely mechanical considerations led to the view that the same mechanical forces which led to the origin of life will also lead to its destruction.

The scientific atmosphere in many mathematical circles today favors a rather different position. The consensus of opinion, at least in some mathematical circles, is that we are fast heading toward a nonmechanical explanation of reality. Jeans expresses this view as follows:

> The universe begins to look more like a great thought than like a great machine. Mind no longer appears as an accidental intruder into the realm of matter; we are beginning to suspect that we ought rather to hail it [that is, mind] as the creator and governor of the realm of matter—not of course our individual minds, but the mind in which the atoms out of which our individual minds have grown exist as thought. [13]

That is, the very atoms of which our material universe consists are expressions in code of the thought processes of the creator mind. *The mathematician is confessing to his conviction that matter is basically a thought existing in a super mind, consciousness and intelligence which conceived it.*

Conceptions of this kind fit a great deal of the experience we human beings have with our own thought. For our own creations express to a certain extent the mind which conceived them. If we develop this line of thought we can go a long way to resolving the ancient stumbling block known as the dualism of mind and matter, which suggested that matter is hostile to and destructive of life and mind in our universe. For this mathematical conception of matter as the embodiment of the mind behind it not only agrees with ancient thought on the subject, it would go further. [14] *The mathematical conception of the nature of matter would not result*

in the conclusion that mind is a pure function and appendage
of matter, which is what, in essence, most scientists of the
materialist persuasion believe. For they hold that if matter is
arranged in certain specialized ways, it will produce mind and
consciousness. We hold that matter is rather, an end product,
manifestation and function of mind.[15]

Thus progressive thought is leading scientists to conceive of matter as being molded in a kind of thought matrix which upholds matter after having produced it, as the expression of mind and consciousness. There is, as already mentioned, a faint parallel to this in the functioning of our own minds and consciousnesses. The human mind gives itself expression in creations, in which order is increased and entropy reduced. But, just as the expressions and creations of our own individual minds are fleeting and imperfect, they reflect us, the fleeting and imperfect ones. We are bound by the second law of thermodynamics. Our entropy is steadily increasing up to dissolution at death, physically speaking, so that the fruit of our thought will be truly expressed in the fleeting, temporary nature of all we produce. In a similar way, the permanent and substantial character of the enduring mind behind nature will be expressed by the durable character of matter and energy, which cannot be destroyed.

We are not saying that Mind is Nature or that Nature is Mind in such a way that the two concepts cannot be differentiated. On the contrary, we believe that Mind is outside Nature though certainly transcending and pervading it. Thus, we can consider Mind as having conceived of Nature in "itself" and realized it outside "itself" while still pervading it from the multidimensional sphere of omnipresence.

Jeans expresses this idea admirably: "Modern scientific theory compels us to think of the creator as working outside time and space, which are a part of his creation, just as the artist is outside his canvas. 'Non in tempore, sed cum tempore, finxit Deus mundum.' "[16]

There are a few more matters concerning the nature of reality, thought and consciousness to which we must give a little attention before returning to our main theme.

THE UNIVERSE—A THOUGHT IN CONSCIOUSNESS

In the final analysis, Jeans considers the whole universe to be one super-thought in a creator mind and consciousness. The various aspects of matter, including those aggregates of matter which constitute a primate brain, are considered to be subexpressions of that same consciousness and mind. All the properties which matter in its various forms and aggregates can bear are, similarly, expressions of that same mind.

This means that, if we find certain aggregates of nerve nets showing the properties of consciousness and intelligence, even this consciousness and intelligence are expressions of the super-thought in which matter lies as in a matrix. There can be no mere mechanical explanation of thought, intelligence or consciousness in applying this concept of their nature. For their nature and origin are both embedded in the matrix of creator-thought which conceived and maintains them.

The same concept applies to the nature of life itself. If certain aggregates of matter manifest life, this life is also a sub-thought in the super-thought which is the matrix of all matter, including that on which life rides. Here again, there is no question of any mere mechanical concept of life such as that which we find in scientific materialistic conceptions of life.

The same concept can be applied to the act of creation itself. The whole of time can be considered as an act of creation. The latter is merely the materialization of thought in that mind. This means that time itself and all its divisions into centuries, years, months, weeks, days, hours, minutes and seconds are also manifestations out of the thought matrix in which all reality is embedded in the divine mind.

Since some scientists have gained this much insight into the nature of reality and thought, is it not a retrograde step to consider any purely mechanistic theory of thought and consciousness as adequate? This is the more so when we remember that thought is, as a basic creative force of the universe, far too important to be susceptible of such a facile explanation as the purely mechanical one. Here again, Sir James Jeans is an admirable spokesman:

> Mechanics has already shot its bolt and has failed dismally, on both the scientific and philosophical side. If anything is destined to replace mathematics, there would seem to be specially long odds against it being mechanics. [17]

The conclusion that Jeans draws is that we cannot avoid the evidence that *the universe exists in the matrix of controlling thought and consciousness and that this thought is in some ways like our own.* The resemblance between the controlling influence behind reality and our own minds seems to be especially close when it comes to thinking and expressing mathematical reality. This being the case, it becomes manifestly unlikely that biology, and particularly man's central nervous system, stumbled into the universe by chance. *Man's mind and its functioning resemble the functioning of Mind behind reality far too closely to be accidental.*

This similarity between the functioning of our own minds and that of the Mind behind things has caused much thought in mathematical circles. Sir James Jeans expresses the view that, on the basis of this fact of similarity, mind itself, together with thought and consciousness, cannot be a chance intruder into our material world. That is, they are unlikely to have arisen on any truly random basis. The material properties of atoms and molecules alone offer an insufficient basis to account for them. The rather more intangible property known as "thought" must be called in to supply the only possible explanation. In this connection, Sir James Jeans writes:

> While much in it [the universe] may be hostile to the material appendages of life, much also is akin to the fundamental activities of life; we are not so much strangers or intruders in the universe as we at first thought. [18]

The upshot of all this is that *mind cannot be regarded any longer as accidental* (as the Darwinians have always maintained) *but that mind is causal. It is the cause behind the matter and coding around us and the mind within us. In the last analysis, mind would seem to be the creator and governor of reality as well as of matter.*

DESIGN—THE EVIDENCE FOR MIND AND CONSCIOUSNESS

The evidence for mind, then, when everything is reduced to a common denominator, is the mathematical evidence of design and coding. Design is the expression of mind, the same as coding is. For design lies behind all mathematical formulae and equations. Where no design, coding or order exists there is no mathematical expression of thought. Mind is eventually behind every code, both its conception and its reception.

1. James T. Culbertson, *The Minds of Robots, Sense Data, Memory Images and Behavior in Conscious Automata,* pp. 1-466.

2. Ibid., pp. 231, 250-51.

3. Ibid., pp. 376, 381.

4. Ibid., p. 71.

5. Ibid.

6. Ibid., p. 78.

7. Ibid., p. 106.

8. See also A. E. Wilder Smith, *The Drug Users,* pp. 152 ff.

9. Ibid., pp. 149 ff., 152 ff., 165 ff., 171 ff., 213-21, 251.

10. Sir James Jeans, *The Mysterious Universe,* pp. 143-46.

11. Ibid., pp. 146-47.

12. Ibid., pp. 150-51.

13. Ibid., p. 158.

14. "Ever since the creation of the world his invisible nature, namely his eternal power and deity, has been clearly perceived in the things that have been made" (Rom. 1:20). That is, matter manifests thought.

15. Sir James Jeans, pp. 158-59.

16. Ibid., p. 155, "God created the world with the help of time but not in time."

17. Ibid., p. 156.

18. Ibid., p. 159.

9.

consciousness and the space/time continuum

On the basis of the foregoing considerations, all purely mechanical and therefore material explanations of consciousness must be inadequate. They are inadequate to account for even matter itself, which is certainly better understood than consciousness. Accordingly, we must search for evidence on the nature of mind and consciousness beyond purely mechanical and material considerations. This means that we shall have to be prepared to look outside the space/time/energy/matter continuum within which most of our science is practiced today.

It was Sir James Jeans once again who pointed out the route we have to take if we wish to attack the problem of mind and consciousness on a rational and mathematical basis. A concept that this mathematician used to probe into the complexities of consciousness was that of the world-line which illustrates the area of research which we must now enter.

First it will be necessary to define the concept behind a

world-line, since it is vital in order to obtain an overview of our subject.

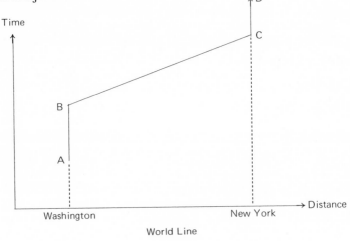

World Line

Figure II

DEFINITION AND EXAMPLE OF A WORLD-LINE

Consider the flight of an airplane from one city to another. Its position before, during and after flight may be represented by a graph (Fig. II) which includes the plane's parking time before takeoff and after landing.

Time AB is spent parked at Washington Airport.

Time BC is spent in flight between Washington and New York.

Time CD is spent parked at New York Airport.

The world-line of the aircraft is designated by the line ABCD. That is, the trajectory of the world-line represents the movement of the aircraft both in respect to time and to space. The world-line represents the progression of the machine in terms of distance (space) and in time. That is, the world-line represents movement in the space/time continuum.

It should be noted that there is no such thing as standing

still in a space/time graph such as a world-line, for the object "standing still" with respect to distance is still moving with respect to time. During the time spent parked at the airports, the world-line moves vertically upward. When the plane is flying, the graph inclines more toward the horizontal position. However, the world-line can never become completely horizontal, for that would imply infinite speed, which, of course, can never be attained. At the speed of light the world-line would approach the horizontal position, but never quite attain it.

To use another illustration of a world-line (which may be far more complex than that of a parked and flying aircraft) consider the space/time graph of a tethered cow or goat. The animal will move around its tethering peg as time proceeds. Thus the shape of the world-line of an animal in such a situation will be helical.

WORLD-LINES AND CONSCIOUSNESS

Culbertson in his theoretical work on consciousness relates the passage of interrelated nerve impulses through interconnected nerve nets to the perception of events in space/time continua. This he relates to consciousness in the following manner: As the interconnected nerve impulses follow their world-lines through a nerve net, they follow a course which is a space/time continuum. They pass through the nerve net so as to produce a three-dimensional/time track which is a reproduction in the "nerve net psychospace" of the central nervous system, or a model of it.[1] That is, the outward event occurring exogenously to the body is reproduced endogenously in the psychospace. A replica of the external event is thus produced internally in the psychospace in neuron impulse form as world-lines in a space/time graph on the nerve net. For the passage of the neuron impulses through the space/time nerve net is really the same thing as a world-line graph. The passage tracks the movement of the neuron impulses in the same way in which we tracked the movement of the aircraft in the space/time continuum. Thus a replica of the exogenous world-lines of outward events is reproduced endogenously in the psychospace of the brain nerve nets.

Otherwise expressed, external reality in space/time is reproduced in replica in world-lines in the psychospace of the human (and other) brain in the form of an internal space/time neuron event. Thus the nerve nets in the central nervous system and in machines designed to experience consciousness are so constructed that neuron impulse events take place there in minature on world-lines in psychospace. In short, the brain is an instrument for the reproduction of external world-lines internally, in miniature. These internal world-lines are projected as an image in the brain nerve nets just as time/two-dimensional space images are projected on a television screen.

As we have already pointed out, Culbertson's research has been devoted to the design of nerve nets capable of receiving such an image. He has been aiming at the construction of artificial psychospaces which he believes will be conscious by virtue of the fact that an image is projected onto them. At this point we hope to combine our previous conclusions with a new one, namely, that consciousness and images in the psychospaces are connected with the concept of world-lines. It is necessary to attack the problem this way, although some repetition is unavoidable. For the concepts of world-lines, psychospaces on nerve nets and neuron images in space/time continua are vital for any concept of the nature of consciousness.

According to Culbertson the criteria necessary to produce artificial consciousness in a machine are quite simple and well defined. Neurons, or circuits, must be so connected that impulses passing along them duplicate, internally and in miniature, world-lines of the outside event. As the impulse flows through the nerve tree it will produce the effect of gradually rising to consciousness until it reaches its full force, after which it passes through the nerve tree to its extremities, thus simulating the fading of an impression. This mechanism is thought by Culbertson and others to explain how upcoming thoughts and consciousness of impressions gradually give rise to the concentrated "now" which becomes the fading past as the impulse passes out to the extremities of the nerve net. The whole nerve tree functions as a substrate on which events appear stereoscopically in space, as well as in time, internally as on a four-dimensional screen, which is the nerve tree.

To produce such an effect of consciousness requires, of course, innumerable neurons and interconnections. For the perception of the passage of time is gained by the lag in impulse passage time as the impulse passes through the nerve axis. This effect of time lag requires great lengths of nerve axis so that the time taken for a nerve-impulse passage becomes a significant factor in producing the time-fading effect. The lengths of nerves needed to get the time effect are, however, not the only factor. In order to obtain the three-dimensional effect, innumerable cross-connections are required too. For these reasons, according to Culbertson, a brain capable of consciousness must be enormously complex. At this point, theory certainly fits in with what one finds in practice.

All this detail is concerned with obtaining a three-dimensional space/time impulse world-line image in a psychospace. What is not explained is how this complex screen becomes actually conscious of the image so marvelously projected onto it. Here again it is perfectly clear that Culbertson's purely mechanical explanation of consciousness is inadequate and begs the whole real question of consciousness and its nature.

FURTHER WORK ON THE NATURE OF CONSCIOUSNESS

Jeans makes use of the concept of world-lines to clarify and develop our understanding of the nature of consciousness. He points out that *the world-lines of the atoms of which the human body is constructed possess the special capacity of conveying sense data to our minds.*[2] Those atoms and molecules forming part of the human body thus, by some mechanism not yet understood, affect our consciousness directly, whereas all the rest of matter outside the particular human body with which we are concerned and its world-lines can affect our consciousness only indirectly. The world-lines of atoms outside our body can only affect our consciousness through the world-line of those atoms which are part of our body and relate to consciousness. Thus the external world of which we are conscious can only penetrate our consciousness by means of the world-lines of our internal constituent atoms.

As a result of these basic considerations, Jeans concludes that our consciousness can best be interpreted as something residing outside our own world-lines but making contact with the outside world-lines at points along our own world-lines. Perhaps an illustration used by Jeans will make this important point clear.

Jeans likens time to something spread out from the beginning, when the universe was "wound up" by the intermediary of the creative act, and stretching on toward eternity ahead of us! He compares this "something" which is "spread out" to a large picture with which we are in contact for only the fleeting instant of consciousness in the "present," just as a turning bicycle wheel is in contact with a long road spread out before it only at the point where it touches the road surface. The road continues to exist both before and after the fleeting instant of contact with the passing, turning wheel.

In a similar way, the world-lines of the atoms of the universe are spread out like a road and continue to exist both before and after we have experienced them in the "now" of consciousness. The "now" is the point of contact of our world-lines (the wheel) with them (the road). The important point in this analogy is that consciousness is considered to exist as just the fleeting moment of contact between our own world-lines and those of the atoms of the universe around us. That is, consciousness occurs at the temporal point of contact of two sets of world-lines—our own and those of reality around us.

This picture would give a discontinuous view of consciousness if we did not connect it with other capacities of the central nervous system. Continuity of consciousness attained by memory images of previous contact of our world-lines with those of universal world-lines. Memory helps us to recall each fleeting moment of contact. By extrapolation forward we may be able to "see ahead" for a short period and envisage the road ahead, the future, while we are still in the contact of the "now."

Such pictures help us to understand how human consciousness consists of a central "now" bolstered by the recall of the memory-induced consciousness of the past. In some rare cases human consciousness may possess the faculty of extrapolating forward into reality and thus experiencing points of the world-lines of universal atoms which have not yet made contact with our world-lines. The "prophet" can thus see the future with the same clarity with which ordinary mortals see the memory of the past, and the "now." As we have pointed our elsewhere, certain hallucinatory drugs such as mescaline, tetrahydrocannabinol (cannabis, hashish, etc.) and LSD are apparently capable of catalyzing the human central nervous system in the exercise of such faculties.[3]

According to this picture, our consciousness touches the universal picture only along the world-lines belonging to the atoms of which the human is composed. This concept brings with it a very important insight. Other people's consciousness may touch the same world picture as we are touching and experiencing at exactly the same time. And other people experience the same world-lines as we do but only by the intermediary of their own particular world-lines. This means that everyone's consciousness is an exclusive, private, individual experience even though each of us touches a common picture of universal world-lines. Thus it comes about that we all live and die in a kind of isolation from each other. We are all "congenitally" lonely due to the very structure of our consciousness. The only thing we have in common is the reality with which we can be in contact.

As the picture of consciousness changes with the changing of our contact with the "road," the image of the passage of time results. In fact, it looks as if we are being dragged along our world-lines as we go through life and fleetingly experience various portions of the universal space/time reality at the sequential points of contact which our world-lines make with the universal ones.

There are a number of consequences to these views. Weyl develops this concept of consciousness and describes events not as though they just "happen." He points out that it would be nearer the truth to say that we "happen upon" universal events in the course of our passage through reality.[4]

Perhaps this way of looking at things could explain some ancient and modern theological views which maintain that the Creator knows the end from the beginning and vice versa. But, in spite of this logic, it would never be correct to take a further step and maintain that life must therefore be regarded fatalistically: "What is predestined to happen will happen regardless of what we do about it." In the East one sees the consequences of this view. The fruit of such a *Weltanschauung* (lethargy, fatalism, laziness) is the best proof that the theory behind it must be somehow wrong. Indeed, it cannot express the whole truth on the problem because it ignores the equally important aspect of human responsibility for altering certain situations and preventing certain undesirable events from taking place.

In other words, into multidimensional reality an extra dimension must be built which will assure what might be termed "free will." It must be constructed so as to assure us that the universe could not be mistaken for a robot toy in process of fulfilling an unalterable, set program in the course of its running down.

Plato brings out practically the same idea when he says in *Timaeus* that the past and future are created species of time which we unconsciously but wrongly transfer to the eternal essence.[5] We say "was," "is" and "will be," but the real truth is that the only really valid term which we dare use in the face of eternity is the one we call "is"—just as God, the Eternal, calls himself the "I am."

On this basis, consciousness may be considered as a double

event in just the same way as the touching of the road by the bicycle tire may be considered as a double event. One side of this event is the touching of the road by the tire. The other side is that of the touching of the tire by the road. So my consciousness consists of the atoms of my world-line coming into contact with the exogenous universal world-lines outside my body as well as the external world-line, representing the whole universe, coming into contact with my world-line.

In this view, *consciousness is a hybrid structure arising where the internal and external world-lines meet in the fleeting present. The exogenous lines include the whole of reality, potentially speaking, coming into contact with all of my potential reality at one point in time, the "now." A consequence of this view is that human or other consciousness cannot be said to consist of myself and my material body alone. It is a hybrid between all reality and my reality.*[6] If all reality and I myself are only material, then consciousness could be said to be material—my matter combined with that of all matter external to me. But what about the exogenous Mind or Thought behind the codes of life and matter which we have already discussed? If this Mind is supramaterial, then, on the above basis, my consciousness is also hybridized.

We must conclude then that consciousness, my consciousness, is made up of, or is the result of, the union of myself, plus all matter, plus Thought or Mind behind the universe and its world-lines.

Another consequence of the views set out above is that time, in the shape of the fleeting present, is, as it were, the mortar which builds or holds together the structure of consciousness. In order to possess and experience consciousness in this sense, my portion of the hybrid must come into contact with the external, universal portion. Jeans expresses this idea in the following sentence: "We can most simply interpret consciousness as something residing entirely outside the [universal] picture, and making contact with it only along the world lines of our bodies."[7] Extending this view a little, we may regard consciousness as a hybrid between our bodies with their world-lines and all the world-lines exogenous to them at a position in time known as the present—or the "now." Where consciousness is, there all reality meets potentially with all of an individual's consciousness.

As far as is now known, the immediate mediator of consciousness is our organic, physiological, material brain. The parts mediating this consciousness are described mathematically—not yet physiologically—by the world-lines of the atoms of which these parts consist. Science regards the parts of the brain which carry out the mediation as part of a space/time continuum definable in purely mathematical and material terms. As far as we concern ourselves as scientists with the first part of consciousness, we are dealing with something perfectly tangible and materially definable. It may be that someday we shall be able to analyze it physiologically.

The difficulties begin when we consider the second part of the hybrid which consists of the external, universal, multidimensional world-line in contact with our limited, three-dimensional/time system. Some implications of these difficulties become apparent when we consider Bohr's theoretical suggestions for the mathematical treatment of phenomena in multidimensional systems. We must look for a moment at these difficulties.

BOHR'S VIEWS ON CONSCIOUSNESS.

Bohr went one stage further with the theoretical basis we have been considering. He suggested that "the minutest phenomena of nature do not admit of representation in the space-time framework at all."[8] This means that the three-dimensional/time continuum of the theory of relativity will explain only some of the phenomena of nature, but by no means all. Thus, large-scale astronomical phenomena and radiation are amenable to Einsteinian theory, but smaller phenomena may have to be explained by abandoning our three-dimensional/time continuum altogether and launching out into multidimensional/time continua.

This finding brings with it difficulties in visualizing the kind of treatment necessary to probe further into the phenomenon of consciousness. For trans-three-dimensional/time continua are probably involved in consciousness and these phenomena do not lend themselves to visualization or experiment. While we may regard that part of the consciousness which belongs to us and our world-lines as possessing merely three dimensions, plus time, the other part of the hybrid known as consciousness, that part belonging to all reality and Mind without us, cannot be so regarded. It is just this part of the hybrid which may involve transdimensional world-lines and will be scarcely susceptible to our own thought processes.

When our own world-lines meet the realities of universal, multidimensional world-lines, a hybrid consciousness is formed which will be, therefore, at least in part, outside the realm of scientific or biochemical inquiry. This simply means that the human mind and consciousness may contain, besides the purely material element, which no one should attempt to deny or reduce in importance, a *transmaterial or transcendental element as well. There is, as a consequence, no difficulty at all, scientifically speaking, in considering man's mind and consciousness to be in some ways finite and material. After all, a man loses consciousness if the carotid arterial blood supply to his brain is cut off by throttling him. But, scientifically speaking, it is just as possible to firmly maintain that man's mind shows definite transcendent attributes and properties, some of which may be extant and eternal even after he has been throttled to death.*[9]

TRANSFINITE CONSCIOUSNESS AND INDETERMINACY

Many scientists, among them Jeans, find no difficulty, as far as consciousness theory is concerned, in leaving the three-dimensional/time continua and launching out into the multidimensional continua. In fact, they point out that the addition of extra dimensions may help to solve many outstanding problems. In this connection, Jeans mentions that even to describe the meeting of two electrons in space requires mathematical data involving seven-dimensional concepts—six special dimensions plus time—if an exact description is to be obtained.[10] The three-dimensional space for each electron is quite separate and only the dimension of time welds them together into one concept.

It is important therefore to keep firmly in mind that mathematical, multidimensional, even transmaterial concepts are often used and have proved satisfactory in supplying answers to many otherwise difficult problems. Even the problem of indeterminacy is reduced to manageable proportions by employing multidimensional thought as Jeans points out in the following illustration.

THE TWO-DIMENSIONAL WORMS AND INDETERMINACY

In order to illustrate how even the problem of indeterminacy can be managed by simply adding another dimension, Jeans uses as an illustration the case of intelligent worms who were congenitally limited to the experience of two dimensions rather than our three dimensions. These intelligent, two-dimensional worms noticed in their perambulations that certain patches of earth with which they came into contact became, for no accountable reason, wet, while other patches remained dry, equally unaccountably. They studied this problem intensively in order to find a rational explanation. For years they recorded and analyzed the distribution, time of occurrence, and size of the wet patches and the relative amount of water in them. In summing up many years of state-subsidized analytical work, they came to the reluctant conclusion that there was no way of knowing in advance which patches of earth would become wet and which would remain dry. Further, there was no way of knowing how much moisture would be present in the wet patches. Nor could they explain in any rational way why some patches never became wet. They had to be satisfied with the unsatisfactory answer that some areas just became unaccountably wet and others remained unaccountably dry.

The result of all this work in our two-dimensional flatland was the promulgation of the theory of indeterminacy which stated that there was neither rhyme nor reason why certain areas of flatland became wet and some did not. Nor was there any satisfactory account to be given of the source of the wetness. No predictions could be made as to where and how much wetness would appear. The principle of indeterminacy was firmly established as the result of this lengthy and expensive research. For two-dimensional worms it proved to be absolutely correct—but only for them, as we shall see.

If we were now able to do a little genetic surgery on the worms with the result that their congenital limitation to the recognition of only two dimensions could be removed, some remarkable things would happen. As soon as the recognition of the third dimension—a dimension which had always been there, though unrecognized by the two-dimensional worms—became possible, our worms would be able to see the sky which they had been congenitally unable to see before the surgery. Now they could actually see the clouds and the raindrops which had caused them all the headache. With this sight their complex theory of indeterminacy dissolved. Even though it was perfectly valid as long as they were restricted to two dimensions, the moment the third dimension, that of height and depth, was added, they could rationally account for some patches of earth getting wet and some remaining dry. The third dimension, added to the original two dimensions, caused the liquidation of the theory of indeterminacy, which was valid for two dimensions only.

May it not be the case that at least some of the problems confronting us concerning consciousness and mind would be solved immediately if another dimension or dimensions were added to the continuum in which we attack the problem? If the mind is in contact with multidimensional continua in the way we have outlined above; if the mind is, as a hybrid, part of transdimensional reality, *then our attempting to compress multidimensional reality into our restricted three dimensions plus time will introduce insoluble problems like indeter-*

minacy. Reducing a three-dimensional world with rain and clouds and height into a two-dimensional world without height produced the worms' Theory of Indeterminacy. So reducing multidimensional reality into our anthropomorphic three dimensions will surely produce problems which are not really present in the original multidimensions.

What we wish to make perfectly clear is that life and consciousness may belong at least in part, in the multidimensional transcendent scene—much evidence speaks for this— with the consequence that, as long as we include only time and the three-dimensional system of matter into our considerations, certain aspects of life and consciousness will be permanently insoluble. That is, materialistic philosophy alone would not be expected to synthesize problems simply because as dimensional truth it is incomplete.

SUMMARY

Thus it has become clear that although consciousness is not limited to biology, it has not yet been produced artificially in machines, nor is its nature by any means fully understood. The theories of consciousness which have been advanced recently are usually based on mechanical considerations and as such must prove to be inadequate.

This position on artificial consciousness and its nature contrasts sharply with the successful research which is being carried out in the field of artificial intelligence. Since the development of our particular hypothesis (on the rationale behind evolutionary processes) depends on intelligence as well as consciousness, we accordingly devote some time in the following chapter to artificial and biological intelligence. We shall then be in a position to develop the synthesis on evolutionary processes which we set out to accomplish.

1. James T. Culbertson, *The Minds of Robots, Sense Data, Memory Images and Behavior in Conscious Automata,* pp. 420-23.

2. Sir James Jeans, *The Mysterious Universe,* p. 126.

3. A. E. Wilder Smith, *The Drug Users,* pp. 204-30.
4. Cited in Jeans, p. 127.
5. Ibid.
6. See also Wilder Smith, pp. 145-49, 242.
7. Jeans, pp. 126-27.
8. Cited by Jeans, p. 132.
9. Wilder Smith, pp. 191-233.
10. Jeans, p. 133.
11. Wilder Smith, pp. 151-232.

intelligence:
artificial
and biological

As we have now seen, consciousness does not need to be coupled to behavior, nor does behavior need to be dependent upon consciousness. They usually are coupled in the human, but this coupling is by no means obligatory. Reflex behavior, for example, bypasses the conscious centers of the brain, thus illustrating a dichotomy in behavior and consciousness even in the normal human.

Let us now investigate the related problem of intelligence as opposed to consciousness. We must begin with a definition of intelligence, for this is vital to the synthesis we wish to develop.

DEFINITION OF INTELLIGENCE

The Computer Dictionary and Handbook defines intelligence as follows: "The developed capacity of a device to perform functions that are normally associated with human intelligence, such as reasoning, learning and self-improvement [related to machine learning] ."[1]

A generally accepted, perhaps wider definition runs: "Intelligence is an ability to profit from past experience."[2] *The Computer Dictionary and Handbook* defines artificial intelligence as:

> The study of computer and related techniques to supplement the intellectual capabilities of man. As man has invented and used tools to increase his physical powers, he is now beginning to use artificial intelligence to increase his mental powers; in a more restricted sense, the study of techniques for more effective use of digital computers by improved programming techniques.

The latter definition means, fundamentally, that basic intelligence resides in the biological (human) brain, but that this faculty may be extended and supplemented artificially. However, some workers in the field are of the opinion that basic intelligence itself can be synthesized and caused to ride on entirely artificial devices without depending on biological intelligence and more than merely supplementing it.

C. A. Rosen points out that a universally acceptable definition of absolute intelligence does not yet exist, but that it may be said that a machine is intelligent "only if it can perform tasks that normally require almost continuous human control . . . in attempting to cope with unforeseen changes taking place in its environment."[3] Rosen then goes on to list such matters as language and communication requirements, problem-solving, planning, pattern recognition, learning and sensing, which, by introspection, also appear to be elements of intelligence. These and other elements of intelligence, together with their relationships to each other, are difficult to pinpoint and assess even today, and in Rosen's opinion they are not likely to be completely clarified in the near future.

Intelligence may have little to do with consciousness, and vice versa; they are not necessarily coupled phenomena. For highly intelligent machines may not be designed to experience any consciousness at all. Presumably a highly conscious organism (or machine) might not be very intelligent. How-ever, since machines capable of learning and profiting from experience can be made, we may maintain that artificial in-telligence is a fact.

There are some important phenomena connected with intelligence, both biological and artificial, which we must examine at this point.

IMPORTANT PHENOMENA ASSOCIATED WITH
BIOLOGICAL AND MECHANICAL INTELLIGENCE

Inference-Making. Frank George, Chairman of the Institute of Computer Sciences, and Director of the British Institute of Cybernetics, was interviewed by *Science Journal* in 1968 on problems related to machine intelligence and on the possi-bility of synthesizing human or android intelligence. His re-marks throw light on the whole spectrum of machine and biological intelligence, so that we propose to cite Dr. George, particularly with respect to an aspect of intelligence known as inference-making. One of the cardinal difficulties still standing in the way of machine intelligence is that of giving the intelligent machine the capacity for making inferences and for reasoning.

Dr. George writes,

> This is fundamental. If human beings—or some features of them—are ever to be created artificially we have to under-stand how they are able to reason. To reason they need a language, and *so language must be a prime requisite of in-telligence.* The problem now is that computers use the for-malized, abstract but very precise language of mathematics, but we human beings use the vaguer, if broader, language of verbs and nouns. It's the gulf between the two that causes all the problems. So one thing we've been doing is to pro-gramme computers to accept stylized English statements and to link this language with logical inference making.

> I want, for instance, to be able to ask a computer: "Is Charlie John's brother?" Commercial computers using stan-dard programs could answer that only if they had written in

their memory the statement: "Charlie is John's brother." We want a computer program that will look for the symbolic equivalents of Charlie, John and "being a brother." It might then find that Charlie is Hilda's brother, that Hilda is John's sister and that it has a description of brotherly and sisterly relationships which enables it to infer that Charlie is indeed John's brother. The computer knew it all along but had to make inferences to get there. That's a process that's a lot different from the way computers normally answer questions and it's much nearer the way humans do it. Then, of course, it's only a question of hardware to design a machine that will speak rather than type at you, and listen to, rather than read, what you have to say.[4]

This brings out an extremely important point in modern computer design and capacity: The present generation of computers lacks the ability to make inferences. At present, computers must have in their memories precisely defined answers with which to answer specific questions. But the making of inferences is, at present, quite beyond the reach of the modern computer. No doubt this situation is likely to be altered in the future, for concentrated research is proceeding in this field.

Pattern Recognition, Insight and Imagination. Besides the capacity for insight, there are other important distinguishing marks which still divide human intelligence from machine intelligence. Among these distinguishing marks are the vital abilities to create and recognize patterns. This is one of the most important problems which require solution if artificial intelligence is ever to approach the breadth of spectrum shown by human intelligence. Dr. George has also discussed this problem.

A human being is capable of looking at a crowd of people and of seeing just one single person in it while ignoring all the others in the crowd. Computers can be programmed to see and to take in the whole scene. They can absorb all the facts about the crowd with which their input devices provide them. However, although a computer may have an enormous capacity for the facts of the crowd—in some cases exceeding that which a human brain can deal with—yet the computer is not very clever at distinguishing the important from the un-important, or at distinguishing the single individual from the mass.

The human brain is able to distinguish and to discriminate. It can concentrate on the important matters and ignore the rest. Research is proceeding intensively at present with a view to elucidating the mechanism by which humans effect this feat of concentration which is bound up with the wider prob-lem of pattern recognition.

It is held in many circles today that imagination, as well as the ability to draw inferences, is an important part of the capacity for intelligence which will have to be grafted into computers if artificial intelligence simulating human intelli-gence is to be able to ride upon them.

Fundamentally, imagination is really nothing more than a special kind of pattern recognition. It is the ability to mix up ingredients so as to form new mixtures, combinations and recombinations, which give rise to new patterns. Old ingredi-ents are blended into new relationships and contexts. Thus, it is obvious that pattern recognition and imagination are close-ly related and that these attributes are connected with such creative abilities as composing music or writing poetry.

Thus it is not surprising that this property, which might also be designated a form of insight, is perhaps the most difficult one to build into a machine so as to enable it to exhibit true intelligence of an artificial but broad spectrum. A computer today could be programmed to paint a picture, write a piece of poetry, or compose a piece of music. How-ever, as things stand, such a machine could not, in general, be programmed to carry on these activities entirely indepen-dently and on its own initiative.

Emotion and Personality Simulation. One of the reasons why it is so difficult to get a machine to do such things as to write true, original poetry, compose an aria, or paint a picture of the midnight sun over Lappland, is due to the fact that the machine possesses no emotional systems to back it up. Much artistic creation depends upon true emotions and feelings—attributes which present-day computers simply do not possess. True artistic creations which are dependent on emotion will, therefore, not be likely to emerge from any machine brain until emotions have been simulated in its programming. Work is proceeding in this direction today.

Having now scanned some of the various aspects of artificial and biological intelligence, we are in a better position to look at the basic requirements which have to be met in order to design machines showing broad-spectrum artificial intelligence.

BASIC REQUIREMENTS FOR BROAD-SPECTRUM ARTIFICIAL INTELLIGENCE

In order to elucidate the various requirements for artificial intelligence such as we have mentioned above, John Lochlin, of the University of Texas, has been developing his "Aldous" program. This program represents an effort to synthesize robots which will possess not only the artificial intelligence of the orginary computer but also such supplements to its intelligence as the emotions of hate, love, ability to appreciate the "good" and to abhor the "bad."

It will be appreciated that, although these emotions are essential in order to build a machine showing human characteristics, yet they are by no means vital to the simulation of mere intelligence itself. One must remember that the basic requirement for artificial intelligence is concerned with the ability to develop self-programming or self-adaptation, so that a machine can profit from experience, which is the basic requirement of intelligence according to our previous definition.

Although the "Aldous" program involving the grafting of emotions onto computer intelligence is important in order to build a well-rounded computer character and intelligence, yet it is not vital to the problem of pure intelligence itself. The real problem is concerned with the further development of self-learning, self-adaptation and self-programming machines which can profit from past experience and possibly reprogram themselves up to bigger and better robots, using their own "metabolic" energy to do so.

Frank George believes that it is just at this point (self-programming) that progress will be made in the near future. Programs which are self-adaptive and self-modifying, according to the nature of the problem put to the machine, will be further developed.[5] Success in this direction has already been obtained in the design and construction of chess-playing machines which can now be programmed to play a chess game of international match standards—and win. This feat is due entirely to the self-adapting programming which modifies the course of action which the machine takes according to the moves the opponent makes. One could never guess just what the chess-playing machine will do in its next move, for its course of action alters with every move the opponent makes.

In the very nature of the case of the chess-playing machine, no algorithm can be developed for the game of chess. The machine can play the game in an entirely unpredictable way. In other words, the machine is, in an entirely independent manner, able to profit from the experience it gains from the moves carried out by its opponent. Thus it exhibits true artificial intelligence within the scope of our definition.

Judging by the results of research obtained up to date, there appears to be, in theory, no upper limit to the degree of artificial intelligence that could be designed into machines of this type. Such a statement, however, should not be interpreted to mean that man can, at present match or even approach, his own intelligence by the use of artificial means. This is not yet possible in the present state of the art for the simple reason that, although the machine can outstrip man's intelligence in certain narrow areas, yet the machine cannot reach or outstrip the breadth of man's intelligence. We look into this question a little later.

At present it is difficult to measure human intelligence and compare it with artificial intelligence, owing to this difference in the breadths of spectra between the two. The human mind is unequalled in its ability to make inferences and recognize certain pattern forms—singling out one man in a crowd pattern and concentrating on him alone; whereas machine intelligence is unrivaled in its ability to calculate rapidly and accurately.

One of the aims in computer science today is to construct machines capable of handling concepts—even strictly mathematically expressed concepts—rather than simple binary data. It must be remembered that even the most abstract concepts are expressable in simple binary formulation. The machine is thus able to solve abstract problems by simply doing sums, which is a quite different method from that adopted by the human brain to solve abstract problems. However, if a machine could be constructed which is capable of handling concepts rather than merely simple binary data—with the reservation made above, that concepts may be *expressed* as binary data—then we should be approaching the deductive and inductive inference-making capacity which resembles that used by the human mind.

Even though the above is true, yet one must still keep Karl A. Koler and Murray Eden's warning firmly in mind: "The brain is not a computer, not does it work the way a computer works. Cells are not vacuum tubes, or transistors, or even integrated circuits."[6] The brain may arrive at similar results to those reached by a computer but it certainly uses a different route to get the same answer. For the computer uses the computation route. The brain, on the other hand, uses such faculties as pattern recognition and inference-drawing to arrive at its answers. It is also capable of producing endless new patterns and concepts if we let its imagination run wild. Even the most advanced chess-playing machines lag a long way behind human intelligence in their ability to recognize patterns and concepts.

In order to systematize these differences in spectrum

breadth of intelligence in the human brain and the computer, the following table is given.

THE BRAIN AND THE COMPUTER COMPARED

The strong and weak points in the performance of the human brain and the computer may be compared under the following headings:

Human Intelligence	Computer Intelligence
1. Mathematical calculating ability relatively slow and somewhat inaccurate	Mathematical calculating ability rapid and accurate
2. Inference-drawing capacity and reasoning power highly developed	Inference-drawing capacity and reasoning power relatively poor
3. Ability to concentrate on the important while ignoring the unimportant highly developed	Poor at distinguishing the important from the unimportant
4. Uses the broad but often vague language of verbs and nouns	Uses the precise language of mathematics
5. Power of pattern recognition, imagination and insight highly developed	Pattern recognition, imagination and insight capacity relatively poorly developed
6. Strongly developed emotional system—anger, hate, love, humor, joy, fear, sorrow, etc., backs up the power of recognition, imagination and insight	Development of emotion systems still rudimentary

7. Self-programming and adaptive abilities highly developed; profits from past experience (basis of definition of intelligence)	Self-programming and adaptive ability at present under intensive development—as illustrated by chess-playing machines and similar devices

It is thus a well-established fact today that artificial intelligence within the meaning of our definition has been attained. But the spectrum of intelligence which has been artificially produced is still far narrower than that of human intelligence. The narrow spectrum of machine intelligence is only partially compensated for by the great accuracy and speed with which it works.

UNSOLVED PROBLEMS IN ARTIFICIAL INTELLIGENCE

Frank George brings us back to the fundamental problems still awaiting solution before a machine can be designed to do the work of a wide-spectrum biological brain. In this connection he remarks:

> To reason, they [human beings] need language and so language must be a prime requisite of intelligence. The problem now is that computers use the formalized, abstract but very precise language of mathematics, but we humans use the vaguer, if broader, language of verbs and nouns. It's the gulf between the two that causes all the problems. . . . The nub of the problem is making the computer accept English and then making it use it the way we do.[7]

In spite of the real gulf between machine and brain intelligence, it must not be forgotten that tremendous progress has been made in attempts to bridge the gulf. Frank George is careful to point this out while emphasizing at the same time that much remains to be done:

> One shouldn't be misled by the fact that you feed a computer only with very precise arithmetical data; that data can

be made to represent extremely vague generalizations. This is what clever programming is all about. And one shouldn't confuse this with the need to be able to use natural language in man/machine communication. Conceptual analysis—which is the thing that matters most in machine intelligence, with the possible exception of learning—is all bound up with language. But, in the final analysis, the machine itself will always perform arithmetical sums to get its answers.[8]

MACHINE TRANSLATION OF LANGUAGES

The arithmetical basis of the computer need not impair its conceptual ability, provided the concepts can be expressed in a suitable mathematical form for the computer's digestion. In spite of this, the computer language problem is a real one. This fact is brought out by the attempts being made to use computers for language translation from Russian to English and vice versa. In this area, progress has been very disappointing to date. Failure is due largely to the wealth of conceptual capacity embodied in natural human language which is difficult to grasp and formulate in a purely mathematical language. Here, in an area rich in conceptual relationships, the computer, which is by nature poor in handling concepts and inferences, begins to flounder badly.

In discussing the problem of machine language translation with a view to future developments, George quotes Dreyfuss as having commented, when questioned on the possibilities of solving such conceptual problems with machine aid, that because a few people have climbed some very tall trees they think they can solve the problem of getting to the moon.[9]

RELATIONSHIPS BETWEEN INTELLIGENCE AND PATTERN RECOGNITION: ANDROIDS AND PARTIAL ROBOTS

Owing to the extreme complexity of human intelligence and its broad spectrum, an effort is under way in the United States and other countries to divide up the problem by constructing various separate organs simulating parts of the human anatomy. The synthesis of the complete android is a tall order. Therefore the synthesis of the intelligent hand-eye machine is being studied in two separate programs. One such program is under way at the Massachusetts Institute of Technology (Professors M. L. Minsky and S. Papert) and the other at Stanford University (Professor J. McCarthy.) [10]

In these programs a mechanical hand with many degrees of freedom and which is capable of grasping, transporting and assembling building blocks of various shapes, is coupled to a television camera viewing the area in which the hand operates. The television camera sends its data to be analyzed by a computer which then, by feedback, operates the hand.

This intelligent hand-eye machine is then assigned specific building plans which involve assembling building blocks into desired structures. The assigned tasks involve selection of correctly shaped and sized blocks, and grasping and carrying them to the proper site in the correct sequence. Guidance in this process is provided for the hand-eye machine by models of structures stored in the computer memory. These "simple" processes can be extended to include the use of tools to effect the prescribed construction processes.

C. A. Rosen, of Stanford Research Institute, has extended this idea of the intelligent hand-eye machine by building an automation machine vehicle which, being mobile, is able to react intelligently with its environment on a continuous basis. When it runs up against obstacles standing in its way it can solve the simple navigational problems involved. It continually obtains information useful to itself from its environment.

Before starting an experiment with this mobile hand-eye machine, it is given the opportunity of exploring the laboratory in which it "lives." The floor of the laboratory has been previously carefully littered with solid objects of simple geometric shapes and sizes, such as cubes and wedges. Having absorbed and stored this information on the objects with which the laboratory floor had been strewn, the machine is instructed to proceed to a point in the laboratory which has been predetermined. It is then instructed to push object "A" first to the doorway and then out through the doorway into the outside passageway. If and when the robot bumps into an obstacle, its sensors turn off the drive motors immediately and apply the brakes. This stop mechanism can, however, be subsequently overriden by the controlling computer, so that the machine can be said to possess a primitive "reflex" as well as a "conscious" nervous system.

In the course of further development of this mobile hand-eye robot it is hoped that it will become possible to give the machine its commands in the form of simple English statements using a restricted vocabulary.

This type of research is mentioned to underscore the important fact that the partial robot hand-eye machine, as well as more complete robot vehicles, is both capable of exercising its intelligent capability by making use of *pattern recognition*, in which building blocks are first analyzed by computer for shape and size (pattern) before being recognized as suitable for the construction program in progress, and also of *pattern construction*. From simpler patterns and construction blocks, more complex patterns are constructed. Intelligence is exercised in searching out suitable patterns in order to create more complex preconceived ones. Intelligence is also involved in transporting the smaller, simpler block patterns to new sites and there constructing larger, more complex patterns.

This faculty of machine intelligence to recognize existing patterns and to construct new patterns is being applied today in analysis, recognition and construction of handwritten letters and symbols. Eventually it is hoped that it will be possible to apply the same principles of pattern recognition and pattern construction to the recognition of spoken sentences in English and other languages as well as to the construction of sentences. That is, machine intelligence is to be developed and programmed to recognize speech and its meaning as well as to produce a synthetic vocal language. A machine with these faculties would be able to listen to a conversation and independently answer any problems arising out of such a conversation. One would be able to converse with such a machine as one does with a human being. This goal is, however, still a long way off.

A REVIEW OF SIGNIFICANT FACTORS IN HUMAN AND ARTIFICIAL CONSCIOUSNESS AND INTELLIGENCE

The purpose of the foregoing chapters on consciousness and intelligence has been threefold:

1. To bring out the fact that intelligence and possibly consciousness are not limited to a biological substrate today as they were, at least experimentally, in the past. Machines already show intelligence and may also, as a result of intense research and development, show consciousness in the future. These are new developments about which past formulators of evolutionary theories knew nothing. Obviously they could not envisage the impact these new discoveries would make on evolutionary theory.

2. To demonstrate how pattern construction and pattern recognition are intimately bound up with intelligence itself. To recognize or to synthesize a pattern requires the mediation of intelligence (financed, of course, by calories or energy). All reduction of entropy or increase of order or pattern *requires energy in the form of intelligence somewhere down the line.* It is recent computer research which has extended the definition of intelligence able to do this from the natural field to the synthetic one. Artificial intelligence has given us the tool we need to demonstrate experimentally in the laboratory this relationship between intelligence and pattern recognition and synthesis.

3. To prepare an intellectual bridge which will enable us to relate the pattern construction of a partial robot in the laboratory to the pattern construction we see in the universe around us, both biological and nonliving.

Before leaving these chapters on intelligence and consciousness we can carry out some synthesis in the light of very recent work on consciousness and connected with intel-

ligence carried out by D. F. Lawden, Professor of Mathematical Physics at the University of Aston, Birmingham,
England.[11]

MEASUREMENT OF MIND AND CONSCIOUSNESS

The relationship between the mind and the body has been
discussed for thousands of years by the world's philosophers,
but the results of this discussion have remained nebulous for
the simple reason that no suitable experimental methods have
been on hand to decide between the various theories. Other
subjects of ancient controversy, such as the shape of the
earth, were easily and finally settled once the experimental
methods to decide were discovered.

Lawden does not think that science is sufficiently developed yet to resolve the question of the body/mind relationship in the near future. Even though machines capable of
learning by experience (that is, machines which are truly
intelligent), may show originality of thought and think a
million times faster than a man; even though such machines
may be virtually immortal, yet the question of consciousness
is not so easily solved as is the question of intelligence within
the definition we have used.

Thus, we have made enormous progress toward an understanding of intelligence, but a much slower progress in the
study of consciousness. Intelligent machines, with whom we
may be able to discuss the finer points of exegesis of Holy
Scripture or even the structure of consciousness, are probably
on the way. In fact, it may not be long before such robots
claim to be alive, as human beings are.[12] In this connection,
Lawden describes the film "2001—A Space Odyssey," about a
spaceship on its way to Jupiter. In order to counsel the crew
and provide companionship during the tedium of the voyage,
a computer called HAL was put on board the spaceship. HAL
could *simulate* the feelings and emotions of the crew so con-
vincingly that it was difficult to distinguish it from a true
human. In fact, one interviewer asked the robot whether it
really possessed the emotions and feelings it simulated so

well. The robot's reply was quite illuninating. It said that it honestly did not know!

Dr. Lawden's thesis is that, although HAL may think and may be much more intelligent than the human crew aboard the spaceship, yet the robot is quite unable to feel, that is, to be conscious. The conclusion drawn is therefore quite obvious, for Lawden writes that the robot "throws about as much light on human consciousness as a mechanical shovel."[13]

We have to face up to the fact that, since we do not yet really know what consciousness is, we can hardly expect to simulate it. We understand behavior and can therefore simulate it. But,

> the naive behavioral view which is being advanced by some writers is that a humanoid robot constructed from transistors, whose behavior when its thumb is struck [by a hammer] is indistinguishable in regard to components of the first kind from that of a human being actually experiencing pain. . . . Who can doubt that, if, immediately after the thumb has been struck, the muscles of the victim are paralyzed by a drug, a person will still experience the pain, provided his brain is unaffected, although actually he will appear quiescent?[14]

All this goes to show the same thing, namely, that we are still lacking understanding of the nature of consciousness and cannot yet expect to be successful in generating consciousness artificially.

Some scientists, Lawden among them, believe that there is an absence of strong evidence for discarnate mental-conscious experiences. Such researchers believe that all we can say about consciousness is that the biological brain develops it by principles which we do not yet understand. In order to explain this development of the faculty of consciousness by the brain, it has been suggested that matter itself possesses a basic psychic property which can be strengthened by aggregating matter in certain ways—as in the brain. Just as certain aggregations of matter increase electro-magnetic force, as in electromagnets, and just as forces simulating gravity can be increased by centrifugation, so, it is suggested, is the case of psychic forces in matter. The brain concentrates and magnifies them. Of course, there is no sound evidence that matter does possess such psychic properties, in spite of all that Teilhard de Chardin and Whitehead think to the contrary.

In view of these difficulties Lawden asks himself the following question:

> What are the features of the animal brain which are primarily responsible for the generation of consciousness and which are of secondary importance, not contributing directly to the creation of a stream of experience? If we can isolate the set of features of the first kind, we shall be in a position to decide whether or not any physical system we design also possesses these essential characteristics and therefore will act as a generator of conscious experience. One does not need to repeat the accidents of the internal chemistry of say the neurone, to attain this end, of course. This chemistry is probably conditioned by terrestrial chemical exigencies. Any system which produces a set of features responsible for the generation of consciousness could be tested for such, regardless of whether its neurodynamics are biological or transistorized.[15]

Lawden comes down to the root of this problem of consciousness and its generation when he points out that we must have a means of measuring consciousness if we are going to work in this area. We can measure how quickly and how much a machine learns and so measure its intelligence. *But how are we going to measure consciousness?* Lawden maintains that *unless the existence of psychical interaction can be established, the achievement of a scientific account of the phenomenon of consciousness will remain beyond our powers.*"[16]What we need, then, is psychical interaction (consciousness?) and an instrument sensitive to it.

There have been attempts to achieve this end, although doubt exists in many quarters as to their validity. We mention them here for the sake of the total picture. S. G. Soale and F. Bateman have, allegedly, described "non-physical" interaction between two brains in telepathy.[16] Lawden and many others believe that telepathic interaction between conscious brains is a fact beyond doubt today. Therefore, in order to elucidate the question of consciousness and psychic interaction between conscious brains, he suggests that, if telepathy can ever be brought under effective control in the laboratory which is not so at present, it might be shown that all brains are capable of interacting this way, but that the strength of interaction decreases as the complexity of the brain decreases.[17]

The conclusion which Lawden draws and which may help us toward making our synthesis is that it would be reasonable to accept as a fact that *telepathic interaction between two brains is evidence that the two brains are conscious.* The consequence of this proposition is that, *if one could construct two robots which were capable of telepathic communication with each other, those two robots could be said to be conscious. The amount of their telepathic interaction would be the measure of their consciousness.*

Of course, this is pure speculation and nothing more. But when one is working on the frontiers of difficult fields of endeavor, one must permit reasonable speculation. Lawden's purpose in these speculations is simply to develop an objective test for consciousness. Our own view of the matter is that although there may be much to be said for Lawden's efforts to develop an objective test for consciousness, the corollary of his views would be hard to accept. For, if Lawden is correct, then one person who is out of telepathic communication with another could be shown thereby to be conscious! There is more in this matter of consciousness than meets the eye! For, although I have often noticed telepathy between myself and persons to whom I am very close, yet I have little experience of the same phenomenon between myself and my adversaries! Yet, both sides, in the latter case, are highly conscious.

SUMMARY

We have now arrived at the position where the relationship between intelligence, artificial as well as biological, and pattern design can be demonstrated. Intelligence vastly more rapid and accurate than human intelligence can be synthesized, although to date its spectrum is much narrower than that of biological intelligence. *Intelligence, and its coupling to calories, or work, has been shown to be the secret behind overcoming the outworking of the second law of thermodynamics and the accompanying increase in entropy* to which all nature, left to itself, is subject.

It is this factor which has been overlooked in Darwinian and Neo-Darwinian theory and which has caused Eden and others to assert that new natural laws must be discovered before the Darwinian ship of state can be put on an even theoretical keel. Intelligence, coupled to metabolic calories, or work, is the missing factor. As far as we can see, *intelligence is the only phenomenon capable of removing the theoretical difficulties inherent in Darwinian and materialistic theory.*

The question we must now ask ourselves is quite simple: Why has this view not been accepted before? The following chapters deal with this question.

1. Charles J. Sippi, *The Computer Dictionary and Handbook*, p. 156.
2. Dr. Robert A. Lloyd, Harwell, England, private communication.
3. C. A. Rosen, "Machines that Act Intelligently," *Science Journal* (Oct. 1968), p. 109.
4. Frank George, "Towards Machine Intelligence," *Science Journal* (Sept. 1968), p. 81.
5. Ibid., p. 83.
6. K. A. Koler and M. Eden, *Recognizing Patterns, Studies in Living and Automatic Systems,* p. 1.
7. George, pp. 80-84.
8. Ibid.
9. Ibid.
10. C. A. Rosen, p. 109.
11. D. F. Lawden, "Are Robots Conscious?" *The New Scientist* (Sept. 4, 1969), pp. 476-77.

12. H. Putnam, *Robots, Machines or Artificially Created Life*, p. 63.
13. Lawden, p. 471.
14. Ibid.
15. Ibid.
16. S. G. Soale and F. Bateman, *Modern Experiments in Telepathy*.
17. A. E. Wilder Smith, *The Drug Users*, p. 168.

11.
toward a synthesis in the problem of origins

In recent years scientists, in common with other intellectuals, have shown themselves unreceptive to the suggestion of any form of exogenous direction or constraint of matter toward life's order as a solution to the problem of origins. That is, few indeed are the scientists today who are willing to suggest that the arising of order, including life's order, is to be attributed to any extramaterial sources or source.

Any concept of direction or constraint arising from outside matter would seem to hark back to the idea of a God or an intelligence outside nature which controlled and constrained it up to life and its order. In the eyes of most people of higher education today this idea has been relegated to the Dark Ages. Thus, to revert back to an extramaterial explanation of life and its origin is considered to be retrograde, and indeed impossible, in scientific materialistic quarters.

It is understandable, therefore, that thinkers who suffered under the sometimes stagnating, nonprogressive attitude of some religious leaders of over a hundred years ago jumped at the idea of any scientific theory of origins which would throw the whole concept of any extramaterial First Cause into the intellectual wastebasket.

The problem of an all-good God, an omnipotent God, an omnipresent God, an omniscient God involved with the all-pervading evil in the world he allegedly made, occupied the attention of mankind for many centuries without a solution being found. How could a good Deity create evil? The Gordian knot could so easily be cut by maintaining that no God was involved at all; that everything was a mere outworking of material, natural laws, with no supernatural element in it at all. Thus, when over a hundred years ago a postulate of origins which avoided the whole bone of contention about the reality and nature of God, and which denied all divine motivation in the creation of life, was offered the intellectual world, that concept was accepted as just what the doctor ordered. Randomness, natural selection and long time spans —it was so much easier to deal with these subjects than with an intangible, transcendent God with whom nobody could experiment and about whom no one could risk speculations.

Thus, for over a hundred years the prime cause of origins, for intellectuals, has been randomness, long time spans and natural selection. As a consequence even the name of God has been banned from most serious scientific journals ever since. However, as we have already seen, it is only recently that the alternative to divine constraint and motivation offered by Darwinians has turned out to be an inadequate substitute for the older ideas on origins based on Deity.

What is there to replace them both? One finds theories such as biochemical predestination, at which we have already glanced. But a more than superficial inspection of such theories shows that they beg the real question. For if all matter is an algorithm of life and consciousness, which is Kenyon's basic premise, where did the superorder of the algorithm come from? Order and superorder certainly do not arise spontaneously from randomness. Apart from such superficial theories and the related theistic ones put forward by Teilhard de Chardin, nothing else but the basic Darwinian speculation has been offered to us.

The great advantage of the randomness theory of Darwin with its accompanying natural selection and long time spans was that it destroyed the abhorred necessity of divine intelligent activity behind nature. Today, those in progressive circles in mathematics and physics conclude that cybernetic simulation experiments establish the fact that the principles of randomness plus selection plus long time spans cannot and do not replace the earlier concept of extramaterial constraint acting on matter to produce order, including the order of life. One hundred years ago Darwin's hypotheses were not susceptible of experimental and theoretical disproof. Now they are.

It is understandable that before the age of cybernetics many thoughtful people threw overboard the divine-motivation hypothesis simply because points involved in that theory were thought to be contradictory. There was the question of evil in a world that an allegedly omnipotent, all-good Deity created. Such thinkers usually recognized the order, beauty, and even purpose behind much in life. But they were overwhelmed by the evidence of evil cohabiting with the good around us. This reason for rejecting the postulate of divine motivation and for turning to the Darwinian hypothesis as the only viable alternative is, however, invalid on philosophical grounds, as I have endeavored to point out elsewhere.[1]

In the question of resolving the problem of origins we must not let the problem of evil cloud the issue. Both problems are capable of separate solution.

Meanwhile we must return to the question of the light that recent cybernetic research throws on the problem of origins.

CYBERNETICS AND THE PROBLEM OF ORIGINS

We have already mentioned the computer experiments in which the huge time spans postulated by Darwinians have been simulated to ascertain if they will produce, with the help of selection, the order that evolutionary theory demands. We must give details and references to this work at this point.

Dr. Marcel P. Schützenberger has pointed out the importance of these simulation experiments in his article entitled "Algorithms and the Neo-Darwinian Theory of Evolution." Schützenberger writes in this connection:

> I would like to draw your attention [to] the fact that nowadays computers are operating within a range which is not entirely incommensurate with that dealt with in actual evolution theories. If a species breeds once a year, the number of cycles in a million years is about the same as that which one would obtain in a ten-day computation which iterates a program whose duration is a hundredth of a second. Our ability to play with iteration of this magnitude is quite a new thing, and we can begin to develop some concrete experience with this type of progress. It was not so in the time of Fisher and *mon bon maître* Haldane, and now we have less excuse for explaining away difficulties by invoking the unobservable effect of astronomical numbers of small variations.[2]

Schützenberger continues this line of thought:

> Neo-Darwinism asserts that it is conceivable that . . . selection based on the structure of the second space brings a statistically adapted drift when random changes are performed in the first space in accordance with its own structure. We believe that this is not conceivable. In fact, if we try to simulate such a situation by making changes randomly at the typographic level [by letters or by blocks, the size of the unit does not really matter], on computer programs we find that we have no chance [i.e., less than $1/10^{1000}$] even to see what the modified program would compute: it just jams. We can specify what it would take to have the random modification introduced so that a sizable fraction of all programs start working: it is a self-correcting mech-

anism which must incorporate something like a symbolic formulation of what "computing" means. Thus no selection effected on the final output [if any!] would introduce a drift, however slow, of the system toward the production of this mechanism *if it were not already present in some form*. Further, there is no chance $[<10^{-1000}]$ to see this mechanism appear spontaneously and, if it did, even less so for it to remain. Finally, we can predict what would happen if such a mechanism had been installed: for almost all the mutations the computation performed would have no relationship to the ones executed before; hence, no relationship to the selective pressure exercised on the output. All this, I repeat, is a simple consequence of the lack of matching between the space of the outputs and the space of the programs. . . . *Thus, to conclude, we believe that there is a considerable gap in the neo-Darwinian theory of evolution, and we believe this gap to be of such a nature that it cannot be bridged within the current conception of biology.*[3]

What Schützenberger has endeavored to show is that the reduction of entropy or increase in order as demonstrated by the cell and its genetic code cannot be accounted for on the basis of randomness and selection shifts over millions of years. The reaction to this position by the chairman of the meeting, Dr. Waddington, is quite interesting. He said, "You have confronted us again, you have made the gap because you have left out the middle space, the epigenetic space."

Now, someone (Dr. Wald) was honest enough to ask what Dr. Waddington meant by "epigenetic" space and "epigenetics." It means, of course, the study of the mechanism by which the information contained on genes is transmitted to, and outworked on, protein synthesis. Epigenetics is the study of how this genetic information, in code form on the DNA spirals, is converted into amino acid sequences on proteins. As an example: How does the cell *read* the genetic code to produce sequenced proteins?

To this assertion by Waddington, Schützenberger rightly

replied that it was, compared to the appearance of the original order on the genes, a detail in which we ought not to get lost. The real problem is: How did the code, that storehouse of information, arise originally? Chance will never attain to such order. That is, *the prime question is not, How does a cell read the code? but, How did the cell get coded?* Waddington, probably seeing that Schützenberger's position was impregnable, immediately brought in the proverbial red herring in the guise of epigenesis. As chairman, he directed the whole symposium off its true course (which was leading to the elucidation of the problem of the origin of the order and coding of life). So an argument was interjected on how the cell *reads* genetic codes to produce proteins, about which any self-respecting scientist, Neo-Darwinian or not, will admit that he knows next to nothing! Thus, by a clever subterfuge, Waddington, the chairman of the symposium, confused Schützenberger's real gap in the theory of origins (code origin) with the real gap in our knowledge of how a cell reads the blueprints of protein synthesis on genetic codes (epigenesis)!

Even at this point of confusion in the argument, Schützenberger stuck to his guns and maintained that "in order to mediate between the space of chains of amino acids and the real world of organisms, some new concept has to be introduced, and principles have to be stated explicitly, explaining how this mediation is conceivable."[4] In other words, Darwinian theory does not give any explicit explanation of how spaces between amino acids on a chain become reality in sequenced proteins. That is, "reading" of codes and converting them into real proteins is a feat of the cell which has not yet been explained. Not only was the *reading* of codes not accounted for, but their origin and *existence* was not explained in any satisfactory manner.

Schützenberger insisted that, if the neo-Darwinian theory was in any way to be regarded as satisfactory and complete, one should be able to set the *whole* problem up on the computer, the problem of the appearance of code and its application in reading and decoding in synthesis—seeing we have such highly developed instruments at our disposal today. At this point Waddington's outburst occurred, to which we have already made allusion, "We are not interested in your computers!"

Perhaps it is partly because older theories of origins are turning out to be lacking that some scientists have begun to risk their scientific necks on theories not invoking Darwinian randomness, selection and long time spans. Kenyon, as we have seen, has been reduced to invoking direction from within matter itself to account for the observed order rather than randomness acting exogenously on matter. The risk of collision, on this basis, with the second law of thermodynamics has been pointed out. Teilhard de Chardin has invoked the same principle as Kenyon, but he believed that God made matter so that it was an algorithm of all life and order in the past, present and future. The difficulty with both these postulates is that scientists have never experimentally found a trace of this self-ordering-up-to-life property in isolated nonliving matter. In fact the second law of thermodynamics expresses the universal scientific belief that it does not exist!

THE SOURCE OF CODING INFORMATION

If, now, the Darwinian principles, together with those of Kenyon and Teilhard de Chardin (and all the related principles), are not capable of explaining the order and coding we see both in living and nonliving matter, where can we find an explanation for it?

It is our postulate that to explain this order, we can turn to precisely the same source which we see experimentally at the bottom of all new order today. To order the bricks and wedges strewn around the laboratory floor into a new pattern in the shape of a house, the hand-eye machine exercised *artificial intelligence.* To produce the blocks and wedges of various sizes and colors which served as the basis of the new pattern developed by the artificial intelligence of the hand-eye machine, *biological intelligence* (human intelligence) was applied, though, of course, artificial intelligence would have served as well. Wherever codes, order, reduction of entropy or even reading of codes (translating them into "reality") are seen, there we know from absolutely uniform experience that intelligence has been at work somewhere down the line. We also know that intelligence has to be financed somehow by calories and work. No one would ever dream of accounting for the construction of even such a relatively simple object as a suspension bridge except by postulating intelligence, work and design behind it. *No one would even think of accounting for the simple shapes and forms which the intelligent hand-eye machine built by leaving out the energy-financed artificial intelligence.* The more the complexity of the design is increased, the more intelligence, artificial or otherwise, we shall have to propose to account for it. That is, there will be more energy behind a complex design than behind a simple one.

If this is the case, and it certainly is, from the design behind the simple synthesis of vitamin C upward, then the gap of which Schützenberger has been speaking (the existence of which Waddington and others hotly deny) will have to be bridged by proposing the application of intelligence to supply the explanation both of the origin of life's codes and their realization in reality, that is, their reading.

The difficulty in applying the idea of intelligence to explain codes and their reading is that of where to look for such intelligence. It has been the tacit assumption of scientists since Darwin's time that the only reasoning intelligence to be seriously considered was that resident in the human skull. Obviously human intelligence could not have been responsible for the order in living and nonliving matter, for that order existed long before humanity and its intelligence came into being.

There are three possibilities to which we can turn for a solution of this problem once we see that the intelligence postulate offers the only way out:

1. Intelligence (or a similar psychic property) rides inher-

ently in matter, as Whitehead and his disciples maintain.[5] Evidence for the psychic properties of electrons etc., is, however, hard to come by. Although propounders of these views believe that the inherent psychic properties of electrons, etc., are multiplied as the numbers of particles in living matter are multiplied, and although they believe that an electron in a living organism differs, therefore, from an electron which is not part of a living organism, there is little to say for such theories, except that they represent philosophy and not experiment.

2. Intelligence rode on some form of matter which was external to our universe and in existence before our universe existed. That is, some aggregate of an extra-universal matter possessed intelligence and used it in shaping the order we know both in and on the matter in our universe.

This might be called the "passing the buck" theory, since it pushes the problem back to another, older universe similar to ours but of which we have no knowledge. It has the disadvantage of supposing that another universe, more or less like our own, does exist, has never been located, and is interested in duplicating its intelligence here.

3. Intelligence riding neither in nor on matter as we know it, but existing before any matter or any universe arose, called them into being and up to order. Since we now know that intelligence can ride on such varied substrates as neurons and biological cells as well as on transistors and vacuum tubes, there is little difficulty in believing that it could also ride on other systems, extramaterial or extra-electrical, which are at present beyond our knowledge.

The basis of this line of thought is that it would be ridiculous to imagine that our knowledge of such a subject as intelligence and its substrates is exhaustive, especially since we have been able to experiment with it for only such a short time. We need to keep very firmly before our minds two facts: First, we have experimental proof of the firm existence of super-intelligence all around us in the super codes and order we see on every hand; obviously this intelligence must have existed before we and our order did. And second, since this ordering and coding intelligence existed before us and the matter around which we are built, obviously we should not expect that intelligence to be bound to matter itself, for it made matter. We might expect reflections of that intelligence to show up in matter, but not the real thing itself. *On this basis we should therefore reason that the real thing, the basic coding intelligence behind matter and the life that is constructed around matter, would be, in itself, supramaterial, that is, transcendental.*

REVIEW OF THE THREE ACCOUNTS OF
INTELLIGENCE BEHIND UNIVERSAL ORDER

At this point we can cast a backward glance before leaving these three possible accounts of coding and order.

If account number one were true and matter did possess some inherent psychic property urging it up to life from within, then one would expect other planets of our solar system which consist of the same type of matter as that of which our earth is made to show some signs of this psychic urge in just the same way that matter on earth has, allegedly, shown signs.

In this connection, one would have expected the moon astronauts to have found at least some trace of chemical evolution up to the complexity of life, if such a psychic urge is present in all matter. For the moon contains the same material elements as the earth (although the proportions may differ in some cases).

Here is a real chance for Kenyon and others to prove their hypothesis. But, in all the reports I have seen on analyses of materials brought back from the moon, there has been no evidence brought to light to lend any support at all for the view that lunar matter contains inherent psychic properties urging it forward and upward to the order of chemical evolution.[6] In fact, the following categorical statement was possible: "Scientists studying the samples of lunar soil returned from the moon by Apollo 11 & 12 are united in unambiguously emphasizing that they contain *no evidence of life forms or precursors of life forms.*[7]"

To this must be added the fact that, according to the age measurements made on the lunar material, there has been ample opportunity for such development to have occurred, for the moon is, according to these findings, immensely old. This means that ample time spans have been available to the lunar material to have manifested any inherent psychic urges up toward chemical evolution, at least.

Of the second account, involving a much older material substrate for the intelligence which is to be regarded as the author of our order, all one can say is that no sign of anything of this nature has yet been discovered by modern astronomy.

Of the third account, that the substrate of the first-cause intelligence must be sought in the supramaterial, there is evidence. The fact that materialistic, physical sciences have missed finding such intelligence with *physical* means is surely a proof of its transcendental nature. It is only by reasoning, logic and mathematics, using the most advanced computers available today, that the gap in the purely materialistic Darwinian randomness account has shown up.

One cannot *see*, physically speaking, the intelligent energy that goes into the working out of a vitamin C synthesis. Nor can one physically *see* the intellectual effort that goes into a suspension-bridge blueprint. Yet no scientist would ever deny the presence of intellectual effort just because he cannot physically see it. He *measures* it, in so many man-hours to do so much blueprinting and so many man-hours to realize the blueprint in actual tons of suspension bridge. He knows how to measure the work involved in both the *encoding* process and the *decoding* or realization (reading), process.

If this is so, why should there be difficulty in accounting for the basic *encoding* process by which the blueprint for life was drawn up at archebiopoesis or the beginning of life? Or why should there be difficulty about explaining the *decoding* process by which life is realized by growth regulated by the code on the material genes? In experimental, everyday life, both *coding* and *decoding* are simply and boldly explained in terms of intelligent man-hours. Obviously, then, there should be no difficulty either about the same basic processes in the origin and realization of life. The principles behind both are identical, even though their *scale* of operations may vary a trifle!

Thus the assumption of intelligence to account for origins and maintenance (or realization) of life, does not present any real difficulties *of principle*. Whether the intelligence assumed is artificial, biological or even transmaterial does not offer any real impediment to theory. If we have no difficulties in using this same assumption of intelligence when dealing with pattern recognition and pattern construction in the laboratory and industry, why should we balk at the same assumption when we transfer our field of inquiry to the much grander scale of the universe and its patterns and codes, especially to the code we know as life?

The same principle applies to the patterns and codes behind the atoms with their electron orbits (which decide the patterns of their chemical properties). The chemical patterns on DNA spirals, in their turn, decide the patterns and codes behind the genes and their outworkings in various morphological, physiological and metabolic codes. *Each code and pattern gives rise to another, but they all revert, eventually, in their origin, to the grand code and pattern-maker known as intelligence.*

The difficulties incurred in denying intelligence as the basis of code-order realization are certainly greater than those of assuming intelligence as the author. One is always finally reduced to assuming that randomness gave spontaneous birth to order (the Darwinian position) which amounts to a denial of the laws of thermodynamics and indeed of all laws—for randomness is not subject to laws. But to get around and to avoid the necessity of assuming exogenous intelligence (or Deity), scientists have been willing to commit even this type of scientific hara-kiri, for to deny law is to kill all science.

If, on the other hand, we assume an intelligence behind the codes and order of the universe, we are more or less inevitably forced to assume the position described by our third postulate—that this intelligence must be transmaterial or transcendent. This position has the great advantage of destroying that ancient bugbear of the past which has hindered so many intellectuals in dealing with the Christian position—an anthropomorphic deity, an "old man in the sky." The intelligence we are talking about is ineffable, supreme, supramaterial and time-transcending.

Thus, an intellectual stumbing block which has long stood in the way of intellectuals and kept them from believing in a supreme intelligence has been removed in principle by progress in cybernetic science, since it has been shown that intelligence is no longer bound to human biological substrates. Perhaps it may some day be shown that thought and intelligence, even in the laboratory, are not even bound to electrical phenomena; that they are both the activities of "spirit." For the Holy Book assures us that God is a "spirit" and that they that worship him must do so in "spirit and in truth."[8]

It may be helpful to reflect a moment on certain historical developments related to intelligence, coding and design which took place before and after Darwin proposed his theory.

WILLIAM PALEY AND THE ARGUMENT FROM DESIGN

In the year 1802 William Paley published his famous book, *Natural Theology*. The chief burden of this book was that all nature speaks of the Designer behind it. Just as the existence of a watch proved, at least to William Paley and his friends, the existence of a watchmaker, so the existence of the design we call nature and matter proved the existence of a designer behind them. Paley's celestial watchmaker behind the universe has become proverbial. In consequence of Paley's argument, the very existence of the structured, coded world and life around about us, and of which we ourselves are a part, is a proof of the existence of a designer or God behind them.

The theological application of Paley's thesis became known as "natural theology" and was widely applied in theological circles almost everywhere where thinking Christianity existed. Today most people who have had the benefit of higher education, particularly biological higher education, regard this thesis as outmoded and perhaps slightly ridiculous, tending to anthropomorphism.

Paley's *Natural Theology* was used for many years as a textbook in certain leading British universities as a basis for examination for freshmen undergraduates. Only in comparatively recent years has its use been abandoned. One reason given for the abandonment was that neither the examining professors nor the students believed a word of the whole thesis. Times had changed. Paley and his friends worked on the basis, which was at the time impregnable, that a design proved a designer. But science, particularly biological science, developed with the course of time. Darwinian theory had taken over biological thought by the 1870's and one of the central Darwinian theses was that *design by no means proved a designer behind it.* Design *might* be designed, as it were, but design might also just as easily arise from randomness. In fact, chemical evolution and abiogenesis were considered to be living proofs of this very position. *Darwin had swept away the logic which had been the basis of a great deal of human reasoning since the dawn of history—that design proves a designer.*

From then on the position was thought to be clear. The theologians could no longer base their Sunday morning sermons on the thesis that "the heavens declare the glory of God and the firmament shows his handiwork."[9] Nor could they declare with Paul the apostle that that which could be known of the eternal Godhead of God, his divine nature and almighty power, could be seen in that which was made, namely, the creation.[10] It all became a *non sequitur*. David's psalm about the messages of the created world, "Their voice goes out through all the earth, and their words to the end of the world," was all nonsense, for how could the heavens and their design testify in any convincing way, after Darwin, to the deity behind them?[11]

It is clear that the Old and New Testaments both support Paley's views in an unmistakable way. The very structure of the firmament, in the view of both Testaments, presupposes a designer. Though words and sentences are used neither by the heavens nor by the earth ("there is no speech nor are there words") yet their design proves the designer, who then uses the design to proclaim a message code without words.[12] The heavens and the earth show a *designer* and proclaim the designer's *message* to man. Both of these are aspects of intelligent coding design.

Paley's line of thought had been indigenous to man since the dawn of history. The ancient documents which have come down to us testify to this fact. But Darwin and his friends altered all that. For the first time in history, the glories of the universe, together with the marvels of living matter, *lost their meaning (coding) for man.* Sermons and treatises on the wonders of nature lost their message too. *Even the incredible intricacies of the living cell became devoid of any message to the biologist, who may spend a whole lifetime in the laboratory working on the marvels of life without experiencing any sense of marvel at all. For Darwin had taken the message out of life and its design. Randomness over millions of years was responsible for design, by natural selection, and that's the end of it!*

It is clear that if one introduces randomness (that is, in technical terminology, "noise") into a coded message of any sort, there comes a point at which the message is no longer decipherable. What Darwin did, in effect, was to convert the coded message of the designer into "noise" by maintaining that the whole "code" of life, matter and the universe was, in the last analysis, born of "noise" (randomness). For according to Darwin, randomness has given spontaneous birth to message or code. If a "message" arose in this way from nothing but "noise," then obviously one need not hear nor heed it because there is no intelligence, or meaning, behind it. There is no real significance to the message. It is all mere static!

(One wonders if this is why the present generation seems to love "noise" instead of music. Music is coded, ordered and subject to law. Noise is random and subject to no observable law. The modern human with his radio and television seems to love noise, lawlessness, randomness itself, rather than the beauty of codes and messages from one intelligence to another.)

One reason why it has been possible for such a doctrine as Darwin's to hold sway so long is, of course, that there was no available effective scientific method to test its validity. No actual experiment could be conducted involving the billions of years of randomness, nor could real monkeys be put to strumming on real typewriters for millions of years to see if they did produce Shakespearean sonnets by randomness!

As a consequence, the intellectuals were forced to accept Darwin's word with no actual experimental evidence to back it up. The fossil record was, of course, used as supplementary evidence, but Darwin himself loudly proclaimed its incompleteness. On top of this comes the fact that the fossil evidence we do have is not always transparently interpretable.

Thus, Paley's work was destroyed by a theory for which the experimental evidence was—and still is—lacking. Darwinism survived simply because it was difficult to disprove and because it neatly and conveniently destroyed the divine hypothesis to which intellectuals were unwilling to submit.

THE "SUPER-COMPUTERS"

It is only in recent years, with the advent of the "super-computer" which could automatically, swiftly and surely deal with the astronomical numbers in which Darwin enshrouded his theory, that the denouement of this grand scheme became possible. The astronomical numbers of random changes, the long time spans and the alleged evolutionary "trends" in the midst of randomness have been programmed and fed into super-computers. The result has been dramatic, for the machines jam in their efforts to unravel such tangled masses of informational "noise." No wonder that the mathematical experts have crowded around the site of these experiments just as physicians crowd around the bed of a patient sick of a rare disease, to ascertain the cause of the excitement. The biologists have mocked from a distance and denied the result proclaimed by the mathematicians—that the theory will not work but merely jams the best machines.

PALEY AGAIN—SOME CONSEQUENCES

These fundamental and very recent findings bring with them a far-reaching consequence: Darwin's basic idea was used to sweep away biblical theology as well as Paley's "natural theology" and all theories of nature based upon the relationship of a designer to the design. Up to Darwin's time, few indeed were the thinkers who would have ever seriously questioned this relationship of design to designer. The grand revolt against design and designers was led by Darwin and his friends and marked the end of an age-old epoch in thought. Para- and post-Darwinian thought was based on the postulate that randomness, natural selection and long time periods could produce design just as efficiently as any designer. The result was that theology as well as philosophy had to change to survive the Darwinian onslaught which made Psalm 19 (and many other similar texts) invalid, besides destroying the force of such well-known passages as the epistle to the Romans, chapter 1.

However, in very recent years, the new and radical change we have noted is just beginning to emerge. Darwin's theories which shattered the possibility of a design and of designer relationships, have been found, in their turn, to be invalid. This has been demonstrated by the newest super-computers. What is the consequence? It is that Darwin's erstwhile philosophical victim can live once more. In plain language this means that Paley's hypotheses—and incidentally those of the Old and New Testament Scriptures dealing with this area of thought—can also live again. Paley is reestablished and once more the design is found to throw light on the designer. Far more important than Paley is the fact that by this great resurrection of ancient wisdom, carried out with the help of the computer, ancient theory used by man since the dawn of history and crystallized over millenia for us in the Holy Scriptures, has turned out to be true once more.

JAMMING THE "THOUGHT MILL"

A corollary to the doctrine of "natural theology" as set out in both the Old Testament and the New Testament is rather striking and deserves consideration in passing.

Man's refusal to accept and act upon the doctrine of "natural theology" is plainly stated to be inexcusable.[13] It is inexcusable because the facts of design and designer are self-evident. The position corresponds with all our practical experience in life, so that it is, in fact, an axiom of life. The next step in the argument is a serious one. For, says the writer of the Roman epistle, refusal to accept something which is self-evident (such as the relationship between design and designer) brings with it an inevitable consequence. It has certain effects upon the very mechanism of our thinking, for it amounts to doing violence to the logic inherent in a delicate thought mechanism.

If one puts stones in a coffee mill, the grinders will be damaged. The mill cannot pulverize stones as it does coffee beans. It was not made for such purposes. If a person feeds his thinking processes (or "thought mill") with "stones" (indigestible thought objects, like maintaining that codes and order arose spontaneously out of randomness) these "stones" will "damage" logical thought processes so that the person will become unable to "think straight" ("grind" thought) any more. In the ancient text this thought is expressed by saying,

> Although they knew God [on the basis that design in the universe proves a designer], they did not honor him as God or give thanks to him, but *they became futile in their thinking and their senseless minds were darkened. Claiming to be*

wise, they became fools.[14]

If we see a great design, then we should recognize the great designer behind it. An infinitely great design predicates an infinitely great designer. The rub is that, although this relationship had been known since the dawn of man, many had not taken the time to work out the further consequences— that we ought to spend our lives honoring and serving the designer to the best of our ability.

Thus there are two pieces of logic which must be followed if our "thought mill" is to work properly. First we must recognize the designer-design relationship; and second, we must honor and serve the designer. A logical but delicate mechanism like the brain needs to be fed on sound logic if it is to grow and prosper. But if it is fed nonsense (such as maintaining that randomness spawns code spontaneously) then the logical thought mechanism is damaged and is no longer able to function normally and logically. *It becomes futile in thought and darkened in senselessness.* When one sees the present state of universities, their student bodies and faculties, one wonders if the thought- and logic-deforming process has not proceeded a long way already. For so much that is occurring on our campuses can only be classified as thoroughly illogical and unreasonable. Perhaps this is the result of the "thought mills" becoming damaged by being fed on false intellectual fare for so long!

This process of becoming unreasonable by accepting the unreasonable as our thought basis goes on to a final step which is described by the Roman epistle writer as follows:

> Therefore God gave them up in the lusts of their hearts to impurity . . . because they exchanged the truth about God for a lie. . . . For this reason God gave them up to dishonorable passions. . . . And since they did not see fit to acknowledge God, God gave them up to a base mind and to improper conduct."[15]

One wonders what the designer of a super robot of super intellectual capacity might do if his handiwork insisted on feeding itself with logical and informational nonsense until it was in danger of "blowing its mind." Surely the designer would be expected to take some sort of drastic remedial action? After all, he designed the machine for the sake of producing a sound mind in the first place. If it persisted in negating its very raison d'être by obstinately feeding on intellectual "stones" to the point of destroying not only its own mind but others as well then remedial action would be justified in order to save both the machine and those within its sphere of influence.

Personally, I feel that the much despised concepts of heaven and hell fit into this situation. The Bible speaks pointedly of both. In Romans chapter one, Paul also warns of the dangers of a humanity gone berserk. It speaks of wars and war rumors as a result of this kind of madness which has overtaken mankind. Surely the political and civil chaos in which we find ourselves can only be explained on the basis that man's collective mind is being "blown." Is it possible that the wrong logical and intellectual diet has something to do with it? If so, it is time for our universities to revise some of their courses and methods. If the process of perversion is not checked, man's desperately sick mind will destroy man himself.

The Bible speaks of two types of remedial action. One is the eternal destruction of the individual human mind. The other is the therapeutic action of remedial and vicarious suffering. Under this scheme, heaven would be the realm where minds could grow and flower to their full intrinsic capacity by absorption of the correct intellectual and spiritual nourishment, for which these minds were originally designed.

It is at this point that Darwin's responsibility in the breaking of the link between the logic of a design and its relationship to the designer becomes apparent. The whole concept of design and code arising spontaneously from randomness is not only intellectual and scientific nonsense (from which error a sound knowledge of the laws of thermodynamics could have saved us). It is anti-Christian and atheistic and corrupts intellectual development and morals as well. For freeing ourselves from the restraining guiding hand of the Deity allows moral decay as well as intellectual decadence to occur.

The universities of the world have fed their biological students on intellectual, philosophical and scientific rubbish for nearly one hundred years now. It should give us reason to pause when we recollect that Marxist systems the world over base their total scientific, biological theory squarely on Darwinism. Might we not also remember that wherever Marxism gets to work, there tyranny, oppression, duplicity and all the other signs of moral and intellectual decay set in rapidly? The whole thought process, the basis of reasonableness, as well as the fundament of morals become undermined and deformed if the students of the world and their sensitive "thought mills" are fed on indigestible intellectual and logical "stones" of the type Darwin threw into the world's "thought hopper." Academic leaders are bringing mankind and its order down to disintegration and dissolution by destroying the very logical thought basis on which society has been founded from the dawn of history.

CONCLUSION—SAMSON

We will close this chapter with an illustration. When Samson had been captured by the Philistines he was forced to grind their corn for them after they had put out his eyes. While the Philistines were celebrating their victory they brought Samson, led by a small boy, into their temple to amuse them. Samson knew that their temple rested upon two main pillars and that, if he could destroy these, the temple itself would collapse, killing both the Philistines and himself. So, after a desperate prayer, he took hold of both those vital pillars of the temple. With one last superhuman effort he heaved, and the whole enormous building collapsed as he had calculated it would.[16]

Human society has been built on two pillars since the dawn of time. The first was that the design of the universe showed some designer, spirit or otherwise, behind it, who was to be feared or revered. The second was that the designer expected some kind of order to be set up among man as a result of the order he had set up in the universe. One pillar influenced the other, but both supported the temple of man on earth. Darwin pulled out the first pillar. The result is that the temple of man is fast deteriorating into primeval chaos. The destruction of the fear of God has brought with it the terror of man as the second pillar is being pulled down. Man's "temple" is collapsing about his ears.

1. A. E. Wilder Smith, *Why Does God Allow It?*

2. Marcel P. Schützenberger article in P. S. Moorehead and M. M. Kaplan, eds., *Mathematical Challenges to the Neo-Darwinian Interpretation of Evolution*, pp. 73-80.

3. Ibid.

4. Ibid.

5. Richard Overman, *Evolution and the Christian Doctrine of Creation.*

6. "Summary of Apollo 11 Lunar Science Conference," *Science* 167 (1970): pp. 449-782.

7. *Science News* 97 (1970): 243.

8. John 4:24.

9. Ps. 19:1-4.

10. Rom. 1:20.

11. Ps. 19:4.

12. Ps. 19:3.

13. Rom. 1:20.

14. Rom. 1:20-22.

15. Rom. 1:24-28.

16. Judges 16:23-30.

12.

quantitative considerations and prospects

The reader will have noticed that, in the foregoing, general principles rather than exact mathematical expressions have been set out. This line has been taken because in this particular case mathematical formulae can be best applied after general principles have been established. A general approach has been used, but not because a precise mathematical one is impossible, as has been adequately demonstrated in the computer-simulation experiments which we have cited.

Accordingly, we will now briefly summarize the mathematical relationships existing between entropy and information theory (including coding principles). This skeleton outline which we propose to develop demonstrates the possibility of mathematical quantization of the problems facing the Neo-Darwinians and others in their efforts to produce a reasonable account of the theory behind the evolutionary and abiogenetic processes.

SUMMARIZING THE PROBLEM MATHEMATICALLY

Basically, the Darwinians teach that the information stored on genes and on the chemical compounds on which life rides arose originally by spontaneous random processes operating through aeons on matter as we know it today. We have endeavored to show how implausible such a hypothesis is on general theoretical grounds. It is our task to show precisely why such an assumption, which basically has to do with the mathematics of information theory, is mathematically unsound. We must then go on to develop a sound mathematical theory to cover the known facts.

As we have already pointed out, the second law of thermodynamics states that entropy (the basic measure of randomness, or disorder), *increases with time* in any closed system. In other words, codes and order will, if left to themselves, decrease rather than increase in informational content with time.

This simply means that the sequences and order of a code are perfectly definite entities. Each piece of order conveys a certain amount of information, just as the entities of dots and dashes in Morse code convey exact meaning or information. Now if randomness in the shape of stray dots and dashes is allowed to infiltrate into the coded message, these stray or random sequences will first garble and eventually destroy the message or information.

We could say exactly the same thing in different terms by maintaining that the stray dots and dashes represent an increase in entropy of the code. The perfect code has a high order or a low-entropy status. The entropy of the code rises, and its order decreases as the stray dots and dashes infiltrate into the code, thus gradually destroying its meaning.

This analogy simply shows how information content and entropy status are related. The lower the entropy, or the greater the order, the more information content there is in the code. The situation is like that on the seesaw—as one end goes up (shall we say, the "noise" or "randomness" end goes up), the other end—the information end—goes down. Thus there is a *clear mathematical relationship* between entropy and information, and between information on codes and randomness- or "noise"-destroying information.

Now, genes must be considered to be the very antithesis of randomness. They are chemical structures of a highly ordered, nonrandom nature. Their "orderedness" or "encodedness" conveys highly specific information on the total chemical structure of the proteins making up the organization. Indeed, in the long run, the genes control the total metabolic picture of the living cell.

We can go a step further in this direction. The degree of "orderedness" (or the entropy status) of these genes is directly related to the information content they bear, as we have already seen. In other words, the more information a gene bears, the less random will its structure be. Since randomness is a measure of entropy status, we have, by this means, related the entropy status of a gene to the information which it bears.

There is, thus, a close mathematical relationship existing between information theory and entropy status. This step brings us to communication theory in general as it applies to biology.

COMMUNICATION THEORY

The above relationship between information theory and entropy status interests communications engineers since they are concerned with packing information into the smallest possible "space" for the transmission of messages of information. It is, therefore, the communication engineers and their colleagues in related fields who have worked out the mathematics of the relationship between randomness and information transmission.[1]

Since randomness is a measure of entropy, increasing entropy is the same thing as decreasing information. A gain in information is, in fact, the same phenomenon as a lowering in entropy status. *This means that to convert increase in order or information into a measure of the lowering of entropy status, all we need to do is to change the mathematical plus or minus sign before the equation representing the encoded information or entropy status.*

Ian McDowell, an information engineer, sets this relationship between entropy and the information theory in the following light:

> Communication engineers faced with the problem of coding and transmitting a maximum of information on a given channel have defined quantitatively the information content of a message. The amount of information to be supplied to transmit any given message using symbol x where the probability of any symbol occurring is $P(x) = H(x) = \Sigma\ P(x)$. $\log_2 P(x)$ *which is the negative of the usual entropy formula of thermodynamics.* This represents a definite relationship, and it has been found that the equivalence between entropy in thermodynamics and information in a binary message code is given by the equation: 1 nit [unit of information] = 1.37×10^{-16} erg / ° C.
>
> The degree of order [nonrandomness] in a closed system may be described uniquely, and this description contains a measurable amount of information. As the amount of energy available to do useful work within a system decreases, entropy increases and *the information needed to describe the remaining order in the system decreases at precisely the negative of the entropy increase.* Imagine the traditional "Maxwell Demon" who opens and closes a little door in the wall of a closed vessel containing gas under pressure every time a molecule of gas within a certain velocity range approaches the door, thus sorting out molecules in terms of velocity and decreasing the entropy of the system. Obviously the "demon" must be preprogrammed to do as he does. *The information needed to specify his operation of the door is equivalent to the decrease in entropy within the system which he achieves by that operation. Similarly, the vast amount of information needed to pre-program the decrease in entropy which all living creatures bring into the closed system of the universe*

has been precoded upon the genes of their first parents and could, conceivably, be measured. Evolution, said to begin without any such pre-programming whatsoever, runs counter to the findings of every thermodynamicist and communications engineer. Every thermodynamic closed system approaches the heat death; and no communications engineer ever sent a meaningful message with a monkey at the keyboard.[2]

So much for Ian McDowell, the communications engineer. What he is saying really amounts to the following: Information increase amounts to the same thing as entropy decrease. *When the Darwinians maintain that information has been born spontaneously from "noise," they are practically saying that intelligent coded information and messages arose on a perfectly spontaneous basis from static noise such as we can hear every night on the radio.* Today we can calculate in ergs just how much energy is required to put a certain amount of information onto a channel. *By analogy we could calculate just how much energy in the form of intelligence (information) would be required to put a certain amount of information on the channel we know as the gene or the DNA spiral.*

Molecular biologists are fast unraveling the secrets of the information system contained in the DNA molecule. They are disclosing the secrets of how such incredible amounts of information are stored in such small spaces. *As McDowell so well points out, theoretically it should now be possible to calculate in ergs just how much energy was required to program the first living man or other organism.* The answer would indeed be interesting. Perhaps some communications engineer will do the computation for us on a modern supercomputer. It might supply us with information on the measure of intelligence employed by the Mind behind things to produce life and man!

One thing is certain about the elucidation of these and similar problems: Millions of intelligent man-hours are being expended every year now in merely unraveling the reduced entropy status of the living cell. If mere unraveling requires such enormous amounts of "intellectual horsepower," how much more "horsepower" of the same type must have been needed to actually reduce the entropy status of matter at the first programming of biological life so as to arrive at the first man, animal or plant!

It has been well pointed out by Robert Bernhard that a basic assumption of evolutionary theory is that *"increasing complexity is an essential feature of evolution, but there is no explanation for that phenomenon in the theory."* [3] *This very factor is the crux of the whole question of the missing factor in Neo-Darwinian theory. Information theory requires a programmer to account for the increasing complexity of the whole program of evolution. The theory as it stands provides for no information source to account for the increasing complexity.* Yet it is perfectly clear today that life shows the most complex programs conceivable. *Darwinians dare no longer close their eyes to this basic fact which will require explanation in terms of information theory—the more so as knowledge in this area becomes more generally available.*

UPHEAVAL OVERDUE IN THEORY OF ORIGINS

In summing up, we are now in a position to state that the vast amount of knowledge on hand today concerning entropy status and information theory and their relationship to coding sequences and information on the DNA molecule makes it well nigh incredible that the majority of the world's biologists should still hold tenaciously to the Darwinian dogma of random processes plus long time spans and selection as the basis of abiogenesis and evolution. One can only conclude that the synthesis between information and biological sciences has, apparently, been unsuccessful to date.

It is now clear that information stored on genes must have had its origin in sources other than randomness. *For information is crystallized in programming, and programming flows out of intelligence.* It is clear that intelligence does not originate in the randomness of matter. *It follows, then, that we are standing on the very edge of an upheaval in the theory of origins in general and in biological sciences in particular.* Such upheavals have already taken place in physics and chemistry; they are long overdue in the biological sciences where the dead hand of Darwinism and scientific materialism has weighed heavily on progress for over one hundred years.

It is manifestly unrealistic to hope for change to occur among the older generation of scientists (or even among their younger fellow travelers) whose life's work and reputation are rooted firmly in Darwinian dogma. The symposia we have cited elsewhere surely adequately prove this point. Meanwhile, until the upheaval gathers momentum, theologians and Christians should be wary of modifying their faith to fit in with views of biology and abiogenesis which are overripe for changes. As in other sciences, one supposes that it will be the younger generation of biologists who will fight these changes through—and the older generation which will resist to the bitter end.

INTELLIGENCE AND THE ARGUMENT FROM DESIGN

Assuming, now, that the missing factor in Neo-Darwinian theory dealing with the origin of life and intelligence has been located and that it is related to entropy status reduction and information theory, we must now turn our attention to some developments arising from this position.

It will by now have become apparent that the whole problem of origins, which we have been discussing in the foregoing pages, is intimately linked up with the question of the validity of the so-called "argument from design." Darwinians have maintained for over one hundred years that the presence of a design or pattern is no proof of the existence of a pattern-maker. The pattern, they say, could have arisen spontaneously from randomness, so that the assumption of a designer is superfluous. Before Darwin, the overwhelming majority of mankind did not think this way. The majority held to a belief in the argument from design. It has taken one hundred years of quite intensive endeavor to show that it is Darwin's proposals which are invalid and that, as a consequence, the argument from design *is valid*.

Now, if the argument from design has been revalidated, we must reexamine some of its postulates. One of these was that not only does a design show the *existence* of a designer, but that the nature of the design also gives information on the *nature* of the designer. A simple design allows one to conclude that the intelligence used to produce it need only have been relatively simple. Of course, not all the intellectual horsepower in an intelligence may have been employed to produce each design. But the design can never *overstep* the intelligence behind it.

Looking at the codes behind nonliving matter, one must, with Sir James Jeans, admire the whole concept of matter built up on electron orbits and nuclear structure. Our greatest intellects are still groping to unravel the complexities of these codes. But even these marvels of codes could not go beyond the intellectual horsepower behind them. Looking at the complexities of information systems carried by each of the millions of billions of living cells on the earth at this moment, one cannot but be awed, if not terrified, by the intellectual horsepower that produced such degrees of self-producing coding information. Think of the sheer energy in ergs behind it all!

The source of this coding order behind both the animate as well as the inanimate world must be so superior to any intellectual power that we, mere mortals, have experience of, that for us it can only appear to be infinite. This makes the chances of our finite intellectual horsepower ever coming to terms with that infinite intellectual horsepower very small. And yet, humans are able to communicate with intelligent machines many thousands of times more intelligent than they. How is this done?

Ordinary contemporary computer intelligence is quite unable to understand a command or to absorb information given it in standard English. It uses a mathematical language and we use a grammatical one. *For communication to be established, the language barrier has to be overcome.* The machine or programmer has to learn to translate a command in English into a mathematical language, after which the command is carried out or the question answered and communication and conversation become possible.

THE COMMUNICATION GAP

There are various ways of bridging this communication gap. Either the machine can be programmed to do the translation itself—this is very difficult indeed owing to the vagaries of language—or a programmer is inserted between the machine and the man. The programmer understands English as well as the mathematical language of the machine, and interprets one language in terms of the other. That is, the programmer acts as a sort of priest mediating between man and the machine he has made. At present such a priestly function is essential if communications between man and his own handiwork are to be established.

THE DESIGNER AND THE DESIGNED

Here we have to do with problems besetting communications between the designer and the designed. The "simple" mathematical language of the machine, the designed, does not match, in complexity and flexibility, the language of the designer, who wishes to speak grammatical English to the machine he has designed—but cannot. So the priestly programmer has to be inserted between the two, the designer and the design.

Exactly the same problem would be expected to beset the relationship between the designer behind nature and the intelligently designed part of nature known as man. Obviously the great designer behind the universe speaks a huge number of languages in the expression of his huge intellectual capacity. He speaks, as Jeans said, among others, a mathematical language. But, on top of this, he speaks the chemical language of the elements as well as the languages of physics, geometry, algebra, philosophy and so on. The language of chemistry which he speaks in designing his thought according to DNA coding sequences is a subject in itself. The average human has all he can cope with in maintaining one language with which to communicate. Thus he is likely to be able to absorb only very small amounts of the designer's multilanguage. No one today can be familiar with all the languages of all the sciences. Once more we have the old difficulty of establishing communications between the designer and the designed on account of language barriers.

We, the designed ones, need someone or something to act in the capacity of a programmer, someone who understands perfectly both human language and the designer's language. It is here that the Christian way of life seems to me the most lucid and valid one compared with other religions. For the Christian way teaches that the Designer himself was Christ, who took on himself the form of the designed and lived and died as a man. He learned to speak, as it were, both the languages of the Designer (himself) and the designed. Thus, the Scriptures maintain that there is one Mediator (or Programmer) between God and man, himself a man.[4] He reconciles and establishes communications, explaining the Designer's thoughts in a humanly understandable way. Without his programming, the Designer's thought would be unintelligible to any human. But his translation clarifies the message for us.

I suppose that any inventor who constructed a machine which could understand English and answer in that language, would often spend a nice quiet hour or so of an evening talking to the machine of his bosom, proud of his handiwork and happy in its company! I know that the idea sounds a little naive, but the fact remains that *intelligences seek the company of like intelligences—or like minds.* Would it be so very unnatural to believe that the great Designer seeks, as the Book says he does, the intelligent company of his creatures? Ancient human wisdom spent much time in such communion and was, we believe, richer for so doing than is contemporary wisdom in this age of haste and communications breakdown.

After all, it would be an enriching experience for any one of us to be able to spend some time in the company of a machine, the invention of our own minds, which was, perhaps, many times more intelligent in certain areas than we are. I think I would be enriched by such an experience—as I certainly am when I contrive to spend time with my intellectual human peers. I profit by such occasions. It is hardly surprising, therefore, that ancient wisdom informs us that the communion with our Designer, which we have been discussing, is not only pleasant but is also highly useful. Indeed, the same source informs us with all authority that if a human spends a great deal of time with his Designer, he will so profit from that experience that he will actually become more like his Designer in his attributes.[5]

This idea of being able to talk with artificial intelligence is nothing new or out of the way. Many present-day programs have just this end in view. One can hardly wait for the experience of contact with artificial and superior intelligence in this manner.[6] One wonders what it will be like to talk in an intelligent way to an intelligence which will be apparently quite unconscious. How personal will the machine be?[7]

NATURAL SELECTION AND LARGE TIME SPANS
AS MECHANISMS FOR REDUCED ENTROPY STATUS

We now come to one of the more important difficulties standing in the way of Neo-Darwinian theory. It is this: The process of producing the most complex mechanisms by random changes followed by selection as postulated by Darwinians is an exceedingly clumsy, unintelligent method, to say the least. This method compares, in principle, with setting out to write a book or a sonnet by starting out with a meaningful small phrase, retyping it with a few mistakes, making it longer by adding some more or less random letters and words, and then selecting the lengthened phrases which turn out to be the most useful ones. Repeat this process until the book or poem is complete.[8] Even that ardent Neo-Darwinian, Sir Gavin DeBeer, commented that the Darwinian method of accounting for evolution by this mechanism was "clumsy"; it also involves an astounding waste of effort as well as time.

If all the complexities of nature arose without intelligence behind them, one might be excused for imputing to nature an incredible lack of forethought manifested in the above mentioned way of going about creative work. But, does not the whole intricacy and coding of nature testify to the highest degree of intellectual horsepower behind the design? If super-intelligence is behind things, one would hardly expect a clumsy and appallingly wasteful method such as the one postulated by Darwin to have been chosen for the purpose. Rather, one would have expected the most refined methods of applied intelligence to have been used.

It is just such ingenious methods which we find practiced in the cell. Take, for example, the "zip fastener" mechanism by which a chromosome duplicates itself at cell division. We still have not found out the mechanism by which a cell "reads" the genetic code, translating amino acid sequences on a DNA molecule into real sequenced protein. But the whole feat smacks of the highest intellectual, chemical skill.

It is the "clumsy" aspect of the Darwinian scheme which has disturbed so many thinkers both in the past and present. Who, knowing the facts of the case, would ever be able to bring himself to believe that chance variations in the ignition system of an internal-combustion engine were capable of being responsible for the replacement of the hot-bulb ignition of the early gas engine by the magneto and spark plug of the more developed machines? Would it be possible to bring a person acquainted with the facts to believe that the magneto was replaced by the coil-and-battery approach by randomness, coupled with the pressures of the buyer's market?[9] And yet, far greater coding intricacies have arisen during the development of biology—intricacies so developed that to suggest randomness and time as the solution to the problem of their arising in mechanical fields would be to court the ridicule of all concerned in such development.

To be sure, random methods are possible on paper, perhaps, given enough time and under conditions of nonreversibility such as we have discussed earlier in this book. But the question is, are such methods likely or practically feasible? One can only say that they are too clumsy to ever arrive at any of the delicate intricacies which we see in all nature around us.

The current replacement of the distributer-and-coil method of internal-combustion engine ignition by the electronic-computerized method provides us with one more step in upward evolution, which could never, if one applies the yardstick of common sense, be the result of such clumsy methods as Darwinians propose for far more complex biological evolutionary fact. The only elegant way to account for development of this type makes use of the mechanism which was, in fact, involved in automobile planning and production: namely, some intelligent engineer got down to planning an improvement which was then carried through in the automobile engine. It is only unwillingness to acknowledge an exogenous intelligence behind nature and the universe which prevents us from postulating such an analogous, common-sense cause behind nature.

And yet, biologists ask us to believe that the replacement of a simple blood-pumping tube (as seen in embryos and some worms) first by a two-chambered, then by a three-chambered, and finally by a four-chambered heart, was basically a result of random development acted upon by natural selection over huge time spans. We know today that, physically speaking, the whole embryological development of the heart from a contractile tube upward is controlled by coding and programming on genes. Why should this not have been the case in accounting for the origin of species in history? If we do so account for phylogeny, let us not forget that programming inexorably demands a programmer and a programmer demands intellectual horsepower and energy. Neither should we forget that inanimate as well as animate nature demands a programmer, so that the latter must have been extant before matter and therefore probably transcendent to matter.

THE NECESSITY OF LARGE TIME SPANS
IN THE NEO-DARWINIAN SCHEME

In the construction of a bridge or of a car according to the coded information on a blueprint, the reduction of entropy (the increase in order), proceeds with a rapidity and precision which would be quite out of the question if the same construction were to be carried out by the trial-and-error method. Fabulously long time periods were required for the construction of the first cars and airplanes. Even then, the resulting products were inferior to those we produce today by the blueprint method. In fact, we can probably risk the statement that the more programming and planning behind the building of a car or an airplane or a bridge, the more rapidly —within certain limits—we can construct it.

This simple fact brings with it an important insight: In the last analysis we measure our time units by the rate of entropy increase in the system in which we live. We put sand in the upper part of an hourglass and measure the three minutes required to cook an egg by noting the period it takes for the unlikely, less-random position of the sand "upstairs" to revert to the more likely, that is, more random, position "downstairs." We also measure time by noting how long it takes for a given number of radioactive atoms to decompose by spontaneous explosion. The whole process is really one of increasing entropy, and our time measurements are coupled to it.

Or we can use an example which comes nearer home. Our own bodies are daily wearing out. The time is coming when the molecules of which our bodies are made will revert to a more likely, random state. They will decompose to dust. Entropy will increase and reach its maximum, with respect to our bodies at least, after about threescore years and ten. Time increase and entropy increase are coupled, and we measure time by measuring entropy increase.

If a car is built by the blueprint and code method, that is, by intensive programming with the help of an endless production line, it can be synthesized in an extremely short time. If the trial-and-error mechanism is used, the same synthesis could take ages, figuratively speaking. Such mechanisms are, however, not only slow, but inefficient and clumsy as well. The consequence of this is that time, *as measured by changes in entropy status,* can be "shortened" or even "lengthened" according to the amount of intellectual "horsepower" or programming put behind the entropy changes we are concerned with, in this case the car construction job. By super-programming brought about by the quick application of either super-intelligence or by "compressing" man-hours of "normal intelligence," a car can be produced in a matter of hours. And it is a better car than that produced by years of toil on the trial-and-error basis. That is, high-powered coding, blueprinting and intellectual effort can, in effect, reduce the time required for entropy reduction, which is, in practice, the same thing as shortening time. Which advertiser was it who trumpeted to the world that to save time was to *lengthen* life? He was, within our context, perfectly correct. *For low-power intellectual coding and planning have the effect of stretching out time, while high-power intelligence simulates compression of time when measured in terms of entropy reduction or increase in order and information.*

As a result of these considerations, I, personally, have no intellectual difficulties at all in holding that the universe, and even life itself, could have been synthesized "in a flash." For it is all merely a question of the intellectual horsepower or coding efficiency behind it. Time is measured in entropy increase. Coding represents entropy decrease. To increase entropy more quickly is to make time pass more quickly and to decrease entropy in creation and code production more quickly is to shorten time. *A mighty intellectual force could reduce entropy more rapidly than a weak one.* So, time, entropy and programming are all intimately related. *A super-intelligence needs but a moment to accomplish work we might need ages for.* Therefore, a truly infinite intelligence behind the programming of creation would require no time to do its job; that is, infinitely short time, or a "flash."

Perhaps it is for this reason that the Bible assures us that a thousand years in God's sight are like one day, and an instant may be like an aeon.[10] It all depends upon one's concept of the First Cause and what we think of his intellectual horse-power. Is it possible that those with little trust in him and his intellectual attributes are the ones who are sure that he needed aeons of trial-and-error methods to achieve his work? If he were unintelligent he would *need* aeons! It is true that he *may* have used aeons. From what we know of the universe today, it *looks* as though for some jobs he took aeons. My point is that modern biology has made the use of aeons *a necessity* and a cardinal point of its dogma to overcome the inherent clumsiness of the trial-and-error mechanism it postulates. The supreme coding and programming of all nature should open our minds to the consequences of the factor of intelligence. *For intelligence does things differently—and more quickly!*

EPILOGUE

On the European Continent it has been the fashion for many years now to counter any argument on the relationship of design to designer with the announcement that it is a well-established fact there cannot exist any *proof* of the existence of God. It is quite generally regarded as proof of abysmal ignorance to attempt any line of argument which might savor of any such proof, for it is alleged that no logic can ever lead to any real proof of the divine Being.

This line of thought is, of course, perfectly correct and reasonable if one is prepared to exclude from it evidence attributable to the argument from design. However, if the argument from design rests upon firm foundations, as we are convinced it does, then the bald statement that there can be *no proof* of the existence of God becomes automatically invalid. For, if *design always predicates a designer*, and a stupendous design leads to the predicate of a stupendous designer, then we must come to the conclusion that ancient wisdom in this area was built upon a sound basis. For by extrapolation we can go on to deduce something of the very origin, purpose, nature and destiny of life and its material substrate.

Perhaps we can take a further step. Man is bending his efforts today in the direction of producing artificial intelligence to which he can talk. His tubes, transistors and condensers are all only incidentals—necessary incidentals—in the production of a form of intelligence simulating his own. Such an object is highly worthy of any human intelligence. May it not be, as Teilhard de Chardin thought it was, that the whole purpose of material life culminates in intelligence up to point Omega? All the rest of material nature, the atoms and molecules, the valencies and orbitals, may turn out to be mere incidentals in the attainment of intelligence, just as transistors and tubes are in the attainment of artificial intelligence.

If intelligence and the development of intelligent logic and reasoning is a main purpose of life, then there can only be one worthy aim in our lives. It is to know more about the grand intelligence who designed us—the intelligent ones. The consuming passion of all of life must be to know him. The ancient wisdom encourages us in this passion by providing a Programmer and by informing us that those who strive are progressively transformed into his likeness—if they persevere.[11]

1. See Fazollah M. Reza, *An Introduction to Information Theory;* also D. Middleton, *Introduction to Statistical Communication Theory.*

2. Ian McDowell, Epping, N. S. W., Australia, private communication.

3. Robert Bernhard, *Scientific Research* (Sept. 1, 1969), pp. 28-33.

4. I Tim. 2:5; Heb. 9:12, 15, 24; Gal. 3:19-20.

5. "And we all . . . beholding the glory of the Lord, are being changed into his likeness from one degree of glory to another" (II Cor. 3:17-18).

6. Ernest H. Lenaerts, "Talking to the Computer," *New Scientist* (Dec. 4, 1969), p. 498; also Bernard Meltzer and Donald Michil, eds., *Computer Minds, Machine Intelligence,* pp. VIII, 508.

7. D. F. Lawden, "Are Robots Conscious?" *New Scientist* (Sept. 4, 1969), pp. 476-77.

8. A. E. Wilder Smith, *Man's Origin, Man's Destiny, p. 221.*

9. Ibid., pp. 223-30.

10. II Peter 3:8.

11. II Cor. 3:17-18.

glossary

Abiogenesis. Origination of living organisms from non-living matter; spontaneous generation of life from the nonliving.

Algorithm. The art of calculation by means of nine figures and zero; the art of calculation with any species of notation such as fractions, surds, proportions, etc.; a deterministic set of rules for computing the solution to a set of problems.

Anachronism. A person or event which is chronologically out of place.

Anarchy. A state of confusion or disorder; absence of government or law.

Android. Having human form or characteristics.

Antigen. A substance inducing antibody formation on introduction into the body.

Anthropomorphism. Ascription of human characteristics to things not human; representation of deity with human characteristics.

Aqueous. Of or like water; watery.

Archebiopoesis. The original generation of life.

ATP-ase. A ferment or enzyme specific for adenosine triphosphate synthesis.

Autocatalytic. Self-activating chemical or other reaction.

Biochemical predestination. The theory that life must arise spontaneously from matter without outside interference.

Biodimers. Aggregates of two biomonomers.

Biogenesis. The development of living organisms.

Biomonomer. A basic chemical building block of living material.

Biopoesis. The creation of life from nonliving material.

Biopolymer. Chemical aggregation of biomonomers.

Biosynthesis. The chemical building up of life.

Biotic. Of or relating to life.

Bon mot. A clever or witty aphorism.

Catabolism. Chemical breakdown in living organisms.

Catalase. An enzyme capable of decomposing hydrogen peroxide.

Catalyst. A substance, such as an enzyme, which accelerates a chemical reaction without itself being changed.

Cirrhosis (cirrhotic). The excessive formation of connective tissue, in the liver, for example.

Coacervate. An aggregate of colloidal droplets held together by electrostatic charges.

Condition sine qua non. An indispensable condition.

Congenital. Existing at or dating from birth; constitutional.

Continuum. That which is continuous and selfsame.

Cybernetics. The comparative study of the automatic control system formed by the nervous system and brain and mechanical-electrical communication systems, such as computing machines.

Decadent. Marked by decay or decline.

Defecation. Discharge of undigested food residues from the anus.

Dehydration. Drying; removal of water.

DNA. Desoxyribonucleic acid, an essential substance for life.

Diastereoisomerism. Optical isomerism of compounds whose molecules contain more than one asymmetric center and do not exhibit mirror image relationship (e.g. glucose and galactose, or mesotartaric acid and dextro-tartaric acid).

Dichotomy. A division or splitting into two parts.

Dimerization. The combination of two molecules to form a new molecular species.

Endogenous. Internal; inherent; growing from or on the inside.

Entropy. The measure of unavailable energy in a thermodynamic system.

Extra Sensory Perception (ESP). Perception mediated without the aid of the five senses.

Enucleated. Deprived of a nucleus.

Enzyme. A substance which catalyzes specific chemical transformations, as in the digestion of foods, in plants and animals.

Epigenetic. Development by gradual diversification of an undifferentiated body; the mechanism of development through reading of genetic information.

Erg. A unit of energy or work; the work done by a force of one dyne acting through a distance of one centimeter in the direction of the force.

Etymology. The history of a linguistic form; the derivation of words; a branch of linguistics.

Exogenous. Produced from without.

Extra-human. That which is beyond the human.

Extrapolate. To project by inference from a known into an unknown situation; to project; to extend on the assumption of continuity.

Extraterrestrial. Beyond the earth.

Fehling reaction. A reaction taking place in a solution of copper salt in the presence of reducing sugars or aldehydes to produce red cuprous oxide as a precipitate.

Flowsheet. A diagram showing the successive operations through which material progresses in metalurgical processing.

Gene. A cell entity concerned with the transmission, development and/or determination of hereditary characteristics.

Genetic code. The information code determining heredity.

Heterogeneous. Differing in kind; of dissimilar constituents.

Hiatus. A gap; a break in which a part is missing.

Hieroglyphics. Characters used in ancient systems of writing.

Humanoid. Resembling a human.

Hydrophobic. Rejecting water.

Hydrolyzable. Able to be chemically split by the action of water.

Inherent. Firmly infixed; involved in the essential constitution of anything.

Intrinsic. Belonging to the essential nature of a thing.

Ipso facto. By the fact or act itself.

Isomerism. A condition in which the same chemical constituents are present in the same proportions but in different geometric arrangement.

Macromolecule. A large, complex molecule.

Methodological. Dealing with principles of procedure.

Microbiology. The study of microorganisms.

Microsphere. A small primordial shell of asexual dimorphic *Foraminifera;* a rounded aggregate of matter fortuitously and superficially resembling a living cell.

Millennia. Thousands of years.

Monoculture. Cultivation of a single product or way of life to the exclusion of all others.

Montagnard. Mountaineer; one who lives in the mountains.

Morphogenesis. The formation of differentiation of tissues and organs.

Morphology. The branch of biology which deals with form or structure.

Mutation. A change; a sudden variation in the hereditary code.

Neobiogenesis. The new synthesis of life from non-living material.

Neurodynamics. Energy relationships in nerve cells and fibers.

Neuron. A nerve cell with all of its processes.

Non sequitur. An inference which does not logically follow from the premises.

Nucleic acid. A chemical found in cell nuclei.

Nutrient. That which nourishes.

Obscurantist. One who opposes the spread of knowledge and enlightenment.

Ontogenesis, ontogeny. The life history or development of the individual organism.

Ovum. Egg.

Oxyhemoglobin. The oxidized form of hemoglobin.

Panspermia. A 19th century theory maintaining that life pre-exists throughout the universe and develops wherever favorable conditions exist; opposes the theory of spontaneous generation.

Parabiotic. A situation in which members of two or more species live close to each other without conflict while maintaining separate colonies.

Peptide, polypeptide. The combination of two or more amino acids, the amino group of one acid being combined with the carboxyl group of another.

Permafrost. A permanently frozen layer of soil or subsoil in arctic or subarctic regions.

Photon. A quantum of radiant energy, such as light or X-rays.

Phylogenesis. Related to the development of phyla or larger biological subdivisions of nature.

Plasmogeny. Spontaneous generation of living plasm.

Plethora. A condition of being overfull; excess.

Point Omega. Teilhard de Chardin's phrase denoting the final consummation of all things in Christ.

Polymerization. The formation of macromolecules from simple ones.

Polynucleotide. A nucleotide consisting of a combination of many mononucleotides.

Prebiogenetic. Before the generation of life.

Prebiotic. Before life arose.

Primate. The highest developed species of mammal, including man, monkeys and apes.

Primordial. Primary; fundamental; elemental.

Proteinoids. Protein-like bodies of simpler structure than proteins.

Protobiology. Prehistoric, primitive biology.

Protocell. A primitive, prehistoric form of living cell. Microspheres are sometimes wrongly called protocells.

Psychospace. An area in the mind into which outside events are projected prior to the mind's consciousness of them.

Pyrocondensation. Chemical condensation under the influence of heat and often with the elimination of water.

Quantum. Quantity; amount; elemental unit of energy according to the quantum theory.

Radical. Charged chemical structure.

Ribosome. Microscopic structure in the living cell at which certain chemical syntheses take place.

RNA. Ribonucleic acid.

Scientific materialism. A belief that matter is the only reality and that all of reality can be explained on a scientific basis.

Spherules. Small spheres or globes.

Stereospecificity. Chemical specificity of action dependent on stereoisomerism.

Steric. Relating to the arrangement of atoms in space.

Substrate. A substance acted upon, as by an enzyme; a nutritive medium for growth.

Supramaterial. Beyond or above matter.

Tautology. Redundancy; a needless

repetition of the same meaning expressed in different ways.

Template. A gauge, pattern or mold used as a guide or form for work to be executed.

Thermodynamics. The science which treats of the mechanical action or relations of heat.

Transmaterial. Beyond matter.

Uniformitarianism. The doctrine that existing processes are sufficient to account for all past geological (and other) changes.

Vacuolation. The formation of vacuoles or cavities.

Viscosity. Stickiness.

Weltanschauung. World view; a philosophy which explains the meaning of life as a whole.

Zygote. Fertilized ovum or egg.

index

bibliography

BADAHUR, K. *Synthesis of Jeewanu, the Protocell.* Allahabad, India: Ram Narain Lal Beni Prasad, 1966.

BALL, R. H.; DOROUGH, G. D. and CALVIN, M. *J. Amer. Chem. Soc.* 68 (1946):2278.

BERNHARD, ROBERT. *Scientific Research* (Sept. 1, 1969), pp. 28-33.

BLUM, H. *Time's Arrow and Evolution.* 2d ed. Princeton, N. J.: Princeton U., 1955.

BRUN, J. "Genetic Adaptation of Caenorhabditis elegans (Nematoda) to High Temperatures," *Science* 150 (1965): 1467.

BUTLEROW, A. *Comp. Rend.* 53 (1861): 295.

———. *Ann.* 120 (1861): 295.

CULBERTSON, JAMES T. *The Minds of Robots, Sense Data, Memory Images and Behavior in Conscious Automata.* Urbana, Ill.: U. Illinois, 1963.

FOX, S. W., ed. *The Origins of Prebiological Systems.* New York: Academic, 1965.

FOX, S. W.; HARADA, K.; WOODS, K. R. and WINDSOR, C. R. *Arch. Biochem. Biophys.* 102 (1963): 439; and *J. Amer. Chem. Soc.* 82 (1960):3745.

GAMOV, GEORGE; RICH, ALEXANDER and YČAS, MARTYNAS. "The Problem of Information Transfer from Nucleic Acids to Proteins" in *Advances in Biological and Medical Physics.* Vol. 4. New York: Academic, 1956.

GEORGE, FRANK. "Towards Machine Intelligence," *Science Journal* (Sept. 19, 1968), pp. 80-84.

GROTH, W. E. and WEYSSENHOFF, H. V. *Planet. Space Sci.* 2 (1960): 79.

HALDANE, J. B. S. *Rationalist Annual* 3 (1929).

HERRARA, A. L. *Science* 96 (1942):14.

JEANS, SIR JAMES. *The Mysterious Universe.* New York:Macmillan, 1930.

JONES, M. E.; SPECTOR, L. and LIPPMANN, F. *J. Amer. Chem. Soc.* 62 (1955):819.

KENDREW, JOHN. *The Thread of Life.* Cambridge, Mass.:Harvard U., 1966.

KENYON, DEAN H. and COLE, M. V. *Proc. Natl. Acad. Sc.* 58 (1967): 735.

KENYON, DEAN H. and STEINMAN, GARY. *Biochemical Predestination.* New York: McGraw-Hill, 1969.

KOLER, KARL A. and EDEN, MURRAY. *Recognizing Patterns, Studies in Living and Automatic Systems.* Cambridge, Mass.: M.I.T., 1968.

KRAMPITZ, G. *Naturwiss* 46 (1959): 558.

LANGENBECK, W. *Angew. Chem.* 66 (1954):151.

LAWDEN, D. F. "Are Robots Conscious?" *The New Scientist* (Sept. 4., 1969), pp. 476-77.

LEDERBERG, J. *Science* 131 (1966): 269.

LENAERTS, EARNEST H. "Talking to the Computer," *New Scientist* (Dec. 4, 1969), p. 489.

LOEW, O. *J. Prakt. Chem.* 33 (1886): 321.

———. *Chem. Ber.* 22 (1889): 470.

MARIAN, E. and TORRACA, O. *Intern. Sugar J.* 55 (1953): 309.

MELTZER, BERNARD and MICHIL, DONALD, eds. *Computer Minds, Machine Intelligence*. Edinburgh: Edinburgh U., 1969.

MIDDLETON, D. *Introduction to Statistical Communication Theory*. New York: McGraw-Hill, 1960.

MILLER, S. L. *Science* 117 (1953): 528. ———

———. *J. Amer. Chem. Soc.* 77 (1955): 2351.

MOORHEAD, PAUL S. and KAPLAN, MARTIN M., eds. *Mathematical Challenges to the Neo-Darwinian Interpretation of Evolution*. Philadelphia: Wistar Inst., 1967.

OPARIN, A. I. *The Origin of Life*. New York: Dover, 1953.

———. et. al., eds. *The Origin of Life on the Earth*. New York: Academic, 1957.

———. *Life: Its Nature, Origin and Development*. Edinburgh: Oliver & Boyd, 1961.

ORO, J. *Biochem. Biophys. Res. Comm.* 2 (1960): 407.

OVERMAN, RICHARD. *Evolution and the Christian Doctrine of Creation*. Philadelphia: Westminster, 1967.

PALM, C. and CALVIN, M. J. *Amer. Chem. Soc.* 84 (1965): 2115.

PONNAMPERUMA, C.; LEMMON, R. M.; MARINER, R. and CALVIN, M. *Proc. Natl. Acad. Sci.* 49 (1963): 737.

PUTNAM, H. *Robots, Machines or Artificially Created Life*. New York: Harper & Row, 1966.

REZA, FAZOLLAH M. *An Introduction to Information Theory*. New York: McGraw-Hill, 1961.

ROSEN, C. A. "Machines that Act Intelligently," *Science Journal* (Oct., 1968), p. 109.

ROTHEMUND, P. *J. Amer. Chem. Soc.* 58 (1936): 625.

SANCHEZ, R. A.; FERRIS, J. P. and ORGEL, L. E. *Science* 154 (1966): 784.

Science News. 97 (Mar. 7, 1970): 243.

SIPPL, CHARLES J. *The Computer Dictionary and Handbook*. Indianapolis: Bobbs-Merrill, 1967.

SMITH, A. E.; SILVER, J. J. and STEINMAN, G. *Experientia* 24 (1969): 36.

SOALE, S. G. and BATEMAN, F. *Modern Experiments in Telepathy.* London: Faber, 1954.

STEINMAN, G. *Arch. Biochem. Biophys.* 119 (1967): 67; and 121 (1967): 533.

STEINMAN, G. and COLE, M. N. *Proc. Natl. Acad. Sci.* 58 (1967): 735.

"Summary of Apollo 11 Lunar Science Conference," *Science* 167, no. 3918 (Jan. 30, 1970): 449-782.

WIGNER, E. P. *The Logic of Personal Knowledge.* London: Routledge & Kegan Paul, 1961.

WILDER SMITH, A. E. *The Drug Users.* Wheaton, Ill.: Shaw, 1969.

———. *Man's Origin, Man's Destiny.* Wheaton, Ill.: Shaw, 1968.

———. *Why Does God Allow It?* Eastbourne: Victory Press, 1960.